SDK228 The science of the mind:
investigating mental health
Science: Level 2

The Open
University

D0183641

Book 3
Addictions

This publication forms part of the Open University module SDK228 *The science of the mind: investigating mental health*. Details of this and other Open University modules can be obtained from the Student Registration and Enquiry Service, The Open University, PO Box 197, Milton Keynes MK7 6BJ, United Kingdom (tel. +44 (0)845 300 60 90; email general-enquiries@open.ac.uk).

Alternatively, you may visit the Open University website at www.open.ac.uk where you can learn more about the wide range of modules and packs offered at all levels by The Open University.

To purchase a selection of Open University materials visit www.ouw.co.uk, or contact Open University Worldwide, Walton Hall, Milton Keynes MK7 6AA, United Kingdom for a brochure (tel. +44 (0)1908 858793; fax +44 (0)1908 858787; email ouw-customer-services@open.ac.uk).

The Open University, Walton Hall, Milton Keynes MK7 6AA

First published 2010

Edited and designed by The Open University.

Typeset by The Open University

Printed and bound in the United Kingdom by Halstan Printing Group, Amersham.

The paper used in this publication is procured from forests independently certified to the level of Forest Stewardship Council (FSC) principles and criteria. Chain of custody certification allows the tracing of this paper back to specific forest-management units (see www.fsc.org).

ISBN 978 1 8487 3547 7

1.1

Contents

Chapter 1   The nature of addictions: scientific evidence and personal accounts

Frederick Toates

1.1   What is an addiction?

This book concerns the phenomenon of addiction and considers how biological, psychological and sociological evidence can be brought to understanding it. The first question you might ask is whether addiction is in fact a mental health disorder as opposed to a bad habit or a physical health disorder and therefore something we should be investigating in SDK228. This is indeed a good question and one that has been argued over for some time. You will read about some of this debate in Chapter 3 but for now it is sufficient to say that mental health professionals now regard addiction as a mental health disorder in its own right as well as a problem that can affect health in a variety of ways, such as through indirect effects on the user (e.g. heart problems following excessive alcohol use) as well as on other people (e.g. victims of drink driving accidents).

In Book 1, Section 1.1.1, some characteristics of addiction were illustrated by Mary and her addiction to heroin. Reflecting a general theme of SDK228, it was argued that an understanding of her behaviour required both subjective and objective evidence. This is equally true of the other cases described in the present chapter.

After having set the scene here, Chapter 2 of the present book will look at the common biological effects of addictive drugs and behaviours. Chapter 3 builds on this by looking at a number of explanatory models that have been proposed in order to try to understand why people become addicted, moving towards a biopsychosocial approach. Finally, Chapter 4 considers treatments for addiction.

Addiction presents some particular problems for the investigator. For example, how is the term to be defined? There are numerous ways of defining 'addiction' and it is unlikely that two experts will agree entirely on what the term means. For example, there is heated discussion on what substances and kinds of activity can become addictive. Surely everyone would agree that it is possible to be addicted to heroin but how about nicotine? One can find the argument in the scientific literature that it is the most addictive of all substances (Kozlowski et al., 1989) and yet it was not so long ago that the American tobacco lobby was vociferous in arguing in court that it is not addictive. Can such activities as gambling, love and sex be addictive? Some would suggest that for there to be an addiction there needs to be a substance that is taken into the body, which would, of course, rule these out as candidates. Yet there are charity organisations devoted to helping people who claim to be suffering from addictions to gambling, sex or love. There are new 'tell-all' confessional and self-help books appearing all of the time, describing what it is like to experience one of a range of addictions, or combinations of addictions. So, part of the aim of this book is to introduce you to the controversy that surrounds the issue of addiction and how addictions can be classified, as well as to offer some suggestions as to how you can find a logical way to interpret the evidence.

1.1.1 Epidemiology of addiction

In trying to understand addiction, it is useful to know just how serious and how big the problem is; that is, to understand the epidemiology (Book 1, Section 4.2.5). Unambiguous addictive activities, as related to drugs, cause enormous suffering to the addicted individual, their family and to the broader society. For example: intravenous drug use comes with a risk of acquiring HIV/AIDS; children whose parents are addicted to alcohol may suffer great harm; and much crime is related to the need for those with an addiction to drugs to fund their habit.

But how big is the problem? Of course, here the issue of definition and what to include as an addiction appear at centre-stage. It would also be helpful to know which groups within society (e.g. those of low economic status, people who are alienated from society) are most prone to addictions. Finding such information is not easy. There are statistics on the number of cigarettes and amount of alcohol sold but these do not enable one to estimate accurately the extent of addiction to these substances, as opposed to their controlled use. There are data on drug seizures by police and border agencies. For example, in 2008/2009 a record 241 090 seizures were recorded, which was an increase of 6% on the 2007/2008 figure (Hand and Rishiraj, 2009). Of course, this cannot be linked in any straightforward way to addiction or even drug use. Numbers of people under treatment gives a possible measure of the extent of the problem but of course leaves out all those who refuse treatment or are refused it or who never wish to seek it out. In England in 2007/2008, there were 202 666 people in treatment for drug addiction (Department of Health, 2009). This does not include people under treatment for nicotine or alcohol addiction, which, interestingly, for these purposes do not come under the heading of substances that are being misused. Where an import/sale of goods is not involved, as in addiction to work, gambling, shopping, sex, love or exercise, the problems of getting data are even greater. In some cases, people have tried conducting door-to-door surveys.

■   Can you see a problem with trying to gain information in this way?

☐   People who answer the door are perhaps least likely to be addicted, especially where the activity is illegal. Even if a response is obtained, people are unlikely to tell the truth. A number of people with addictions will be of no fixed abode or homeless or will be in hospital or prison.

The various charity organisations give estimates of the number of people with addictions. It is estimated that some 3% to 6% of the US population show signs of sexual addiction (Gold and Heffner, 1998). Statistics published in 2007 gave an estimated figure of 0.5% of the German population engaging in 'pathological gambling' (Queri et al., 2007), while a Canadian survey found 2% of the population to show what was termed 'problem gambling' (McIntyre et al., 2007).

Indirect measures of use are sometimes termed 'proxy measures'.

We have seen then that there are a number of proxy measures indicating how big the problem of addiction is, but to truly get to grips with addiction it is necessary to consider some terms and definitions, to which we turn next.

1.1.2 Revisiting Mary's addiction

Mary's story (Book 1, Section 1.1.1) can illustrate some terminology that is traditionally associated with addiction. Over time, she required increasingly large doses of heroin to try to maintain its initial subjectively beneficial effect, a phenomenon termed **tolerance**. Without heroin, Mary experienced strong negative emotions and a number of painful bodily effects, termed **withdrawal symptoms**. Although Mary had a period of a year without taking the drug, at a time of great stress she resumed taking it, a feature called **relapse**.

Some people prefer the term **dependence** to addiction, meaning that the individual *depends* upon the addictive activity for some semblance of normality. For example, Mary could only function 'normally' with the help of heroin; hence the notion of 'dependence'. However, all such words are controversial and risk being used in a somewhat pejorative way.

The term 'dependence' creates its own problems. To draw a distinction with 'addiction', a person who has diabetes might be said to be *dependent* upon regular injections of insulin, otherwise their life could be at immediate risk. However, surely no one would say that they are *addicted* to insulin (Alexander, 2008). Similarly, a person who has impaired mobility might be said to be dependent upon a carer but would not be said to be addicted to the services of the carer.

Both 'addiction' and 'dependence' can also be interpreted to imply a sense of passivity on the part of the individual. Mary was something of an extreme case, but she serves to illustrate features that can *sometimes* be associated with the terms 'dependence' and 'addiction'.

To some people, the term 'dependence' suggests involvement of a chemical taken into the body, whereas 'addiction' has a broader feel. Alas, it is not possible to resolve these controversies over the use of language but you should be aware of some of their implications.

1.1.3 How is it decided clinically that someone is addicted?

The ICD and DSM criteria

The World Health Organization in its *International Statistical Classification of Diseases and Related Health Problems* (ICD-10) produced a description of various addictions, all relating to chemicals. (Book 1, Section 4.2.3 introduced ICD and DSM criteria.)

The ICD-10 description for opiate addiction is given as:

Opiates are drugs that include heroin and morphine. They are chemically similar to opioids, introduced in Book 1, Section 3.3.2.

> A cluster of behavioural, cognitive, and physiological phenomena that develop after repeated substance use and that typically include a strong desire to take the drug, difficulties in controlling its use, persisting in its use despite harmful consequences, a higher priority given to drug use than to other activities and obligations, increased tolerance, and sometimes a physical withdrawal state.
>
> *(WHO, 2007)*

Note that, according to this definition, a withdrawal state is not necessarily a component of addiction.

Another source of reference for defining behavioural and mental disorders is the *Diagnostic and Statistical Manual of Mental Disorders* (DSM), published by the American Psychiatric Association (APA, 2000). The latest edition at the time of writing (2010) – DSM-IV-TR – lists seven criteria for deciding whether someone has what is termed a 'substance dependence', which means much the same as an 'addiction'.

Substance dependence is defined in DSM-IV-TR as something that meets three or more of the following criteria within a one-year period:

1 tolerance

2 withdrawal

3 the substance is taken in larger amounts over a longer period than was intended

4 there is a persistent desire or unsuccessful attempts to stop or cut down use

5 a great deal of time is spent trying to obtain or use the substance

6 important social, occupational or recreational activities are given up or reduced because of substance use

7 use is continued despite knowledge that the substance is causing or exacerbating physical or psychological problems.

Meeting the criteria – substance dependence

Based on these criteria, heroin obviously has the potential to become addictive and Mary was unambiguously addicted. However, also based on these criteria, not everyone who uses heroin becomes addicted to it (Alexander and Hadaway, 1982). There are 'occasional users'.

Note that DSM-IV-TR refers to 'substance dependence'. This probably brings to mind drug users like Mary, but the term raises the issue of whether the substance in question might be, say, a type of food (Ifland et al., 2009). Some individuals describe themselves as 'food addicts' or 'food junkies' and the target of their behaviour is refined foods. Kay Sheppard (Figure 1.1) has had a food addiction and has written a number of self-help books on the topic. Vignette 1.1 includes some personal accounts from two of her books.

Figure 1.1 Kay Sheppard who suffered from a food addiction. She has overcome her addiction and has supported others through her self-help books.

Vignette 1.1 Food addiction

Malcolm reports (Sheppard, 2000, p. 11):

> But at an early age I remember feeling frightened and lonely a lot of the time. I was shy and had trouble relating to people. I found comfort from those painful and confusing emotions in food ...

> […] I would get anxious if I thought I couldn't get binge food. It was a relief to find out that they served vanilla wafers and Kool-Aid in kindergarten every morning!

> I soon became seriously overweight and got my first taste of the taunts that all fat children suffer.

The more I was reminded of my inadequacies, the more I ate.

Darla writes (Sheppard, 1993, p. 59):

My mother died soon after and all the feelings of guilt, remorse and regrets were too much to handle without the help of my best friend – food. I went back to eating big time. Within a few months I gained over 40 pounds and was totally insane. I can remember my nightly binges.

I would be shaking so badly and couldn't wait until the spaghetti was cooked. I would eat five or six slices of bread while waiting.

After that I would eat a box of the macaroni product I favoured plus more bread. Some of the shaking would stop, but in a short while it would start again.

Janine writes (Sheppard, 1993, p. 71):

When I walked into a room full of people where refreshments were served, my focus was entirely on the food – how to get by the people, get to the food, and get as much as I could without being noticed! After the party I didn't remember the people but I always remembered what food was served.

My self-esteem plummeted. I felt helplessness, a sense of total failure, self-contempt, disgust, fear and hopelessness. Eating seemed to make these feelings go away temporarily.

Food became my Higher Power and the god I worshipped. Food determined how I felt, what I did and who I was.

The three people featured in Vignette 1.1 reported various features of their addiction. Looking at the reports from a larger population, they meet all of the DSM-IV-TR criteria for addiction, except criterion 5. However, for most people addicted to food, foods of high fat and/or sugar content ('junk food') are no more than a few minutes drive away at a supermarket.

Data for overall consumption of such foods will not give a perfect picture of the extent of any possible addiction but it can serve as a pointer. Table 1.1 shows data for the USA over the period when the obesity epidemic became most evident in that country. It compares data for refined products which are thought to be implicated in addiction, with unrefined products.

■ What trends in food and drink consumption does Table 1.1 show?

☐ A massive increase in consumption of a range of refined foods and drinks that are described as 'hypothesised addictive' but a much smaller percentage increase in consumption of unrefined foods.

The term 'per capita' means 'for each individual'.

Table 1.1 Per capita consumption of refined products (hypothesised addictive foods) and two unrefined products in the USA (from Ifland et al., 2009).

Product	1970 Consumption per capita	1997 Consumption per capita	Absolute increase	Percentage increase/%
Refined products				
Corn and wheat flour	122.0 lbs	172.8 lbs	+50.8 lbs	42
Total caloric sweeteners	122.3 lbs	154.1 lbs	+31.8 lbs	26
High-fructose corn syrup*	0.5 lbs	62.4 lbs	+61.9 lbs	1240
Carbonated soft drinks	24.3 gallons	53.0 gallons	+28.7 gallons	218
Fruit drinks[†]	5.7 gallons	9.2 gallons	+3.5 gallons	61
Frozen potatoes	28.5 lbs	59.0 lbs	+30.5 lbs	207
Chocolate liquor equivalent	3.1 lbs	4.1 lbs	+1.0 lbs	32
Ready-to-eat breakfast cereals[†]	8.6 lbs	14.3 lbs	+5.7 lbs	66
Unrefined products				
Animal protein (excluding eggs)	177.3 lbs	190.3 lbs	+13.0 lbs	7
Beans	7.6 lbs	8.5 lbs	+0.9 lbs	12

* A type of sugar.

[†] These increases may be more significant than they appear, since the reported per capita use includes adults and children, yet most of the usage (based on the nature of advertising of the product) is most likely by children.

Rather unambiguously, certain substances, such as heroin, meet the criteria of addiction as defined in DSM-IV-TR, and refined food is a strong candidate. Might it also be possible to be addicted to activities that do not involve taking a substance into the body?

■ Could you suggest some such activities?

□ The list might include gambling, exercise, shopping, sex and using the internet.

So this raises the question of whether the criteria of addiction could be adapted to include addictions to non-chemical-related activities. The next section will consider this.

1.1.4 Examining the criteria

It is interesting to speculate on why 'addiction' is often defined only in terms of *substance* dependence (as just described). This was not the original meaning of the term, which was based upon the Latin verb *addicere*, meaning 'to yield to' (Alexander and Schweighofer, 1988). In this usage, one could equally well be addicted to, say, love or religion, as to drugs. The more restricted use, which appeared in the 19th century, appears to reflect a 'biomedical view', a response to the harmful effects of certain drugs on some individuals. In such terms and in a biomedical tradition, a body that is disturbed by a chemical intrusion lends itself to a measurable basis of a disorder and presumably a biomedical solution in the form of medicine.

Activity 1.1 Forms of addiction
(LOs 1.1 and 1.2) Allow 30 minutes

Now would be an ideal time to go to the multimedia map and view the video sequence entitled 'Forms of addiction'. In this activity you will find personal accounts from individuals with addictions and from a psychologist discussing the matter.

Let us now look a little closer at some activities that might be called 'addictions', some of which do, and some of which do not, involve taking a chemical substance into the body.

Nicotine

Vic (shown in Activity 1.1), now aged 54, started smoking cigarettes when he was 12 years old and has smoked ever since. He appears to get something good from nicotine. However, note the expression that Vic uses: 'incredibly guilty and ashamed'. His attempts to give up have failed, so guilt and shame have proven to be no match for the pull of nicotine. In some cases, heavy smokers have surgery for heart and lung disease, which they acknowledge was most likely the consequence of smoking. However, even when in hospital, they sometimes sneak out surreptitiously to smoke. When they are without a cigarette, heavy smokers can become very irritable. Smokers will sometimes drive miles to obtain cigarettes. So, can a heavy smoker be said to be 'addicted'?

■   How well do heavy smokers fit the DSM-IV-TR criteria 1–7 above?

□   They appear to fit criteria 1–4. Criterion 5 seems not to be applicable but only because of the ready access to cigarettes. Criterion 6 also seems inapplicable, since smokers (e.g. Vic) can, for the moment at least, function well even when smoking heavily. Criterion 7 applies, since, as exemplified by Vic, smokers fully understand the harm that cigarettes can do to them.

So, based on meeting five out of seven criteria, one can apply the terms 'addiction' and 'dependence' to nicotine use. It encourages a search for similar processes underlying the use of (for example) heroin and nicotine and the search can go further, as follows.

Shopping

Shopping addiction was exemplified by Lawrence in Activity 1.1, who described his strong excitement at the prospect of shopping. Such people find that shopping soothes their minds, particularly at times of stress. People get a 'buzz' from simply acquiring things.

Gambling

Addiction to gambling was exemplified by Patrick in Activity 1.1, who described there being 'no greater thrill' and how gambling solved life's problems. Note that Patrick illustrated vividly the pull exerted on him by the sights and sounds of a betting shop. People addicted to gambling sometimes lie, steal and borrow money from those around them to support their gambling. This can involve casinos and fruit machines, as well as betting shops. The introduction of the personal computer and online gambling sites has made gambling readily accessible. Over time, gamblers often come to place ever-bigger bets in an attempt to reach the earlier highs. On quitting, they feel irritable and restless, their mood being characterised by such terms as 'panic', 'shame' and 'hopelessness'.

Now let us consider some potential addictions not shown in Activity 1.1.

Work

If it can be truly described as 'addictive', work is one addiction that is rather different from the others in that the workaholic is often admired by society. Vignette 1.2 is a personal account from Bryan Robinson, a former professor at the University of North Carolina, also a former workaholic and the author of a book on workaholism.

Vignette 1.2 Work addiction

Bryan Robinson writes (Robinson, 2007, p. 150):

> By the time I was forty, work addiction had invaded every tissue of my body. I was hooked. I was a chain-smoking, caffeine drinking, one-man production line. Like an alcoholic, I felt restless and became irritable when I went more than a few days away from my desk. Even when lounging on a tropical beach, all my thoughts centred on my next project.

Bryan also writes (p. 11):

> [J]ust before we left on vacation, my life partner, Jamey, would search my bags and confiscate any work I planned to smuggle into our rented beach house on the South Carolina shore. But however thoroughly he searched, he would always miss the tightly folded papers covered with work notes that I had stuffed into the pockets of my jeans.

and (p. 12):

> I used to work to defend myself against unwelcome emotional states – to modulate anxiety, sadness, and frustration the way a pothead uses dope and an alcoholic uses booze.

> Since childhood, work had been my sanctuary – my source of stability, self-worth, and meaning and my protection against the uncertainties of human relationships.

Sex

Sex is, of course, another example of an activity that can be perfectly 'normal' but can also get 'out of kilter'. Consider the examples in Vignette 1.3 from both Susan Cheever (Figure 1.2), author of *Desire: Where Sex Meets Addiction* (2008) and Michael Ryan, author of *Secret Life: An Autobiography* (1996) and how they illustrate an element of ambivalence and conflict that features large in addictive activities.

Figure 1.2 Susan Cheever, author of the book *Desire: Where Sex Meets Addiction*.

Vignette 1.3 Sex addiction

Susan writes (Cheever, 2008, p. 127):

> In spite of my love for my daughter, I couldn't seem to stop cheating on my husband, her father. Consciously, I desperately wanted to be faithful.

She also bears witness to the role of stress (p. 128):

> Moving men, doctors, lawyers, book salesmen – any man associated with threatening change in my life became erotically charged, with predictable results.

There is also a good account of the need to introduce variety into the behaviour (p. 131):

> For a while there is no such thing as 'too much' with the object of desire. The world shrinks down to a universe of two.

> When the dose wears off, however, the sex addict doesn't need more of the same person, he or she needs a new person.

Princeton academic Michael Ryan records the strength of the lure and the bodily sensations associated with pursuit of an addictive activity (Ryan, 1996, p. 3):

> It's as if an electronic magnet in my solar plexus were switched on. At its most intense, I'd go into a kind of trance, dissociated, beamed in from Mars, my mouth dry and my heart pounding, my usual waking consciousness hovering somewhere outside my body while I was taken by the pull.

Michael also recorded the investment in time (p. 339):

> I had watched hundreds of porno-movies, some of them in hellish-smelling booths in adult book-stores pumping in quarters every ninety seconds.

Primarily attracted to heterosexual sex, Michael also documents his homosexual activity and here the reader sees the role of stress and the element of ambivalence (p. 330):

> with a stopover in between at a gay bar or porno house where I could pick up a man and have anonymous sex. I had been doing this a few times a year for about two years, and continued doing it during my two years at Princeton – after a girl-friend broke up with me, or when I just couldn't stand being in my own skin.

> [T]o have sex with men, was my deepest degradation. It enacted my calcified childhood shame. Of all my shame-based sexual behaviours, this was the most shameful to me.

Michael also vividly documents the extent to which addiction can take over a life and comparisons with drug addiction come to mind. He uses the term 'disease' to describe it (p. 335):

> [S]exual addiction [is] a disease nobody recognised then and still seems to some people like a joke. It determined what I thought and what I felt. My personality was formed around it. All of my talents, all my good qualities as a human being, were devoted to serving it, and I was willing to sacrifice anything to it.

Michael ends his autobiography with words that give some indication of a factor that can help to maintain addiction (p. 353):

> a lifetime of desperate attempts to feel worthwhile – driving myself mercilessly, clamouring for approval and impossible sexual validation.

Figure 1.3 Peach Friedman, author of *Diary of an Exercise Addict*.

Exercise

Exercise is necessary for good health but like sex it can be taken to excess. If this happens, it can deliver the promise of gaining control over one's life while in reality being a route to loss of control (Friedman, 2009). In Vignette 1.4, Peach Friedman (Figure 1.3), who is now a personal fitness trainer, describes herself as having been 'addicted to running' (Friedman, 2009).

Vignette 1.4 Exercise addiction

Peach Friedman writes (2009, p. 8):

> and [I] started jogging. And lo and behold, I found that I felt better after a hard run.

Peach then started getting up at 5 a.m. to run for six miles or to visit the gym. What started out as valuable exercise tipped into addiction and

Peach records her observation at the gym concerning social interactions with people she knew (p. 30):

> But nobody ever utters a single concerned word about my wasting body and my ritualistic exercise behaviours.

She observes a consequence of her behaviour (p. 54):

> I did know that I was angry at men, at the media, and with my family. I knew that starving and overexercising provided an escape, a way to distance myself from my emotions.

She associated the exercise with pain, even though this was insufficient to deter her, as she records in one day's diary entry (p. 108):

> My pain has eased a bit, but I have to be careful: It returns sometimes without warning, and when it does, it's unbearable. But not exercising is more unbearable, and often the endorphins kick in early enough that I can get through my workout with more exhilaration than pain, and oh, I need that rush, I need that because my life is so pathetic.

Recognising the damage she was doing and trying to take time out from exercising, Peach records a withdrawal effect (p. 129):

> my knees hurt, my hips hurt, my feet hurt, I can't move my shoulder I have beaten my body for years and now I have to stop... I'm hysterical it's withdrawal ... I feel like I'm dying I'm crying ...

Now recovered, Peach advises other people with problems of addictive exercise and notes the danger of relapse (p. 185):

> Running is a popular sport for compulsive exercisers; it's addictive, it's efficient, and it's accessible. I do not generally recommend that an exercise bulimic who was a runner pick that sport up again until she feels solidly recovered. Any practice that was a part of someone's addiction can trigger that person back into that behaviour.

In giving advice, Peach is now able to reflect back on the danger of this addiction (p. 193):

> I also revealed some of the psychological qualities of an exercise addiction: isolating yourself from family and friends; prioritising workouts over social functions, vacations, or holidays; and experiencing extreme anxiety and guilt when unable to exercise.

Those with this addiction sometimes display ritualistic elements, feeling pressure to exercise at certain times and on certain days. If this is prevented, guilt can arise (Friedman, 2009).

Looking across addictions

Considering the range of what might be described as 'addiction', reports of such things as guilt, intrusive images and feeling a 'buzz' or a 'high' represent subjective evidence, whereas the actual behaviour is, in principle, open to objective measurement. It can be useful to consider the similarities and differences between the cases described above and see whether there is sufficient in common to justify use of the general description 'addiction'.

Think about this and a closely related consideration: what is the appropriate framework for understanding and dealing with addiction? Is it the 'biomedical model', based as it is upon observable biological events in the body that are out of order? If this is the case, what kind of treatment is indicated? Presumably, the use of medicines to treat the addiction is suggested, in much the same way that medicine is employed to treat obvious diseases, such as infections with bacteria. Alternatively, is a biopsychosocial perspective needed to make the most sense of addiction?

You might ask whether a legal framework has any relevance to understanding addiction. After all, some of the best-known addictive drugs such as heroin and cocaine are strictly illegal, and, in the USA, alcohol was for a time prohibited, whereas nicotine is perfectly legal. We will come back to this topic in Chapter 4. Insights into the process of addiction can also be gained by comparing and contrasting different addictions, to which the discussion now turns.

1.2 Comparing addictions

1.2.1 Similarities between them

Table 1.2 shows a summary of some addictions and features that are associated with them. While looking at it, reflect on the following issue. On the basis of the accounts given earlier and that of Mary, do you agree that the term 'addiction' is appropriate in each case?

Note: Table 1.2 shows only the *positive* short-term effects and *negative* long-term consequences. There can, of course, also be short-term harmful consequences, such as death from an overdose of drug. Reciprocally, there might also be some positive long-term consequences. For example, workaholism might help achievement of goals. Up to a point, exercise could improve long-term health. The people interviewed in Activity 1.1 do not describe all of the characteristics shown in Table 1.2. Rather, this is a list of some common features shown by people who are addicted.

Table 1.2 Some features of several addictions.

Type of addiction (exemplified by) and [relevant author]	Short-term positive effect	Long-term real or potential harmful consequence	Withdrawal effect experienced
Heroin (Mary; Gary; Robin)	'High'; relief from mental anguish	Harm to the body through physiological effects or crime; loss of income	Goose pimples, nasal discharge, stomach cramps and diarrhoea; low mood
Nicotine (Vic)	Improvements of mood	Harm to the body	Irritability
Junk food (Malcolm, Darla, Janine) [Ifland et al., 2009; Sheppard, 2000]	Numbness, calm	Harm to the body; withdrawal from social activities; inability to care for children; falling asleep at inappropriate times	Fear, anger, disgust, self-loathing
Shopping (Lawrence)	A 'buzz'; soothing	Bankruptcy, capture by police when activity involves theft; disruption to family	Guilt
Work (Bryan) [Griffiths, 2005; Robinson, 2007]	Feel-good factor; 'buzz', 'escape', 'numbing'	Harm to the body; loss of family and friends	Tension, moodiness, irritability
Sex, including use of pornography and internet sex (Susan, Michael) [Black et al., 1997; Maltz and Maltz, 2008; Moskowitz and Roloff, 2007; Putnam, 2000]	'high', 'trance', lowering of anxiety/depression	Disruption to family and position in life; loss of job; capture by police; disease; physical violence	Irritability, insomnia, boredom, guilt, depressed mood
Gambling (Patrick) [Cunningham-Williams et al., 2009; Grant et al., 2009]	Relief of stress, distancing from unpleasant cognitions	Bankruptcy; harm done to family	Panic, shame, anger, guilt, hopelessness, irritability, restlessness, trembling, sweating
Exercise (Peach) [Chapman and de Castro, 1990; Friedman, 2009]	Mood enhancement, 'runner's high'; escape from unpleasant emotions	Physical harm to the body	Agitation; loss of concentration, guilt

What have all these cases in common? In each, there is a powerful pull ('a lure'). That is to say, behaviour is associated with an intention or goal concerning what is to be achieved. In each case, behaviour appears to have been strengthened ('reinforced') by its immediate positive consequences. This outweighs the effects of any longer-term negative ('punishing') consequences (e.g. guilt). Each example involves taking behaviour to excess, as defined by the criterion (7) that there is an element of harm and even destructiveness about it. There is a brief temporary resolution of a problem on getting to the goal (e.g. winning, reaching a 'high' or peace of mind) but the creation of longer-term distress. In several cases, there is a narrowing of the range of behaviours to meet the single goal.

In Section 1.1, you met the term 'tolerance'. There is evidence of tolerance across a range of addictions. For example, gamblers tend to up the stakes over time, whereas individuals addicted to sex tend to increase their risk-taking as in moving to unprotected sex (Giugliano, 2008).

Irrespective of the form of the addiction, the person engaging in an addictive activity behaves in a way similar to someone who has ingested alcohol. Alcohol tends to have an effect termed **alcohol myopia**. This term is used by analogy with myopia in its original sense of short-sightedness. Alcohol tends to make people 'short-sighted' as far as the consequences of their behaviour are concerned. They act to achieve short-term gain but at the expense of long-term cost. For example, under the influence of alcohol, a person prone to violence might seek instant gratification (e.g. to right a perceived wrong) but discount the future costs (e.g. loss of job, imprisonment). Ingestion of alcohol can increase the probability of engaging in further ingestion of alcohol as well as non-alcohol-related addictive behaviours (e.g. sexually addictive behaviour) (Carnes, 2001).

Another feature shared by addictions, though not listed in DSM-IV-TR, is the ever-present danger of relapse: a return to the activity even after years of being 'clean'.

These shared features suggest the value of applying the generic notion of addiction to a range of activities. However, certain differences should not be ignored.

1.2.2 Possible differences

Sharpening the classification

■ Are there any fundamental differences in the activities in Table 1.2 and how they lead to addiction?

☐ As noted, most obviously, some of these activities involve taking a chemical into the body. What is addictive about the other activities must be some consequence that is not associated with taking a chemical into the body.

This is a fundamental difference but investigators need to be on guard against drawing false implications from it, for the following reasons. It is often suggested that addictions should be divided into two classes: *physiological* (also called 'physical') and *psychological*. So-called 'physiological addictions' involve the intake of a chemical and include addictions to alcohol, heroin and nicotine. By contrast, addictions that are said to be 'psychological' involve no chemical intake, e.g. gambling.

■ Based upon Book 1, can you see a problem with a distinction between so-called physiological (or 'physical') and psychological addictions?

☐ If one class is termed 'physiological', then, by exclusion, the other class is '*non*-physiological' or '*non*-physical'. This might lead to the conclusion that such addictions have no basis in the physical brain and no chemical component. In reality, natural mood-altering chemicals could be released within the body by addictive activities.

According to a contemporary perspective, psychological states and brain states refer to two sides of the same coin (Book 1). This means that *all* addictions are phenomena of the brain-mind. From such a perspective, the distinction between addictive activities becomes simply one of the *means* by which the brain-mind is affected: by either (i) taking an extraneous chemical into the body or (ii) triggering intrinsic changes in the chemistry of the body by means of behaviour.

The distinction in terms of 'physiological versus psychological' could also lead to the assumption that psychological factors are not involved in so-called physiological addictions. In truth, as described shortly, social context plays a vital role in all addictions and, according to a biopsychosocial perspective, it mediates its effect via the psychology and biology of the individual. Therefore, the book will not use this system of classification but will simply consider that some addictions are triggered directly by externally derived chemicals and others are not.

Could withdrawal symptoms be used as an argument in favour of the physiological versus psychological distinction? It might be thought that only in the case of addiction to external chemicals, such as heroin and alcohol, does withdrawal manifest in a clear pattern of symptoms throughout the body. Therefore, some psychologists wish to confine the term addiction to dependence on such chemicals. Substances such as alcohol and heroin are indeed well known to be associated with characteristic patterns of withdrawal symptoms that have manifestations throughout the body, such as shivering and sweating.

However, the argument creates serious problems. First, not all chemicals that are described as being 'addictive' are associated with withdrawal symptoms in the tissues of the body. For example, the absence of cocaine in regular users causes effects such as **craving**, an overpowering desire or need (compulsion) to continue taking the drug, and depression but usually no obvious withdrawal-related changes outside the brain.

- ■ Think back to Table 1.2. Are withdrawal symptoms unique to drug-taking?

- □ Drugs such as heroin have particular bodily symptoms. However, in each addiction, people report something like a withdrawal effect, described in such terms as 'irritability' and 'tension'.

Furthermore, there are some reports that individuals addicted to gambling can experience clear bodily symptoms of withdrawal if they do not gamble, much like withdrawal from drugs (Cunningham-Williams et al., 2009). These include stomach upset, sweating and trembling.

Risk-taking

Take another look at Table 1.2 and consider the risks associated with engaging in addictive activities.

- ■ Is there an element of risk-taking involved in each activity such that this might even contribute to the attraction?

□   This is most likely in the case of sex, gambling, drug-taking and shopping (when it involves theft), but perhaps less so in the case of legal activities: addiction to junk food, workaholism and exercise addiction.

Societal attitudes

Think about the attitude of society towards different addictions, as, for example, illustrated by the media.

■   Are there differences in how society views the various behaviours exemplified in Table 1.2?

□   Society tends to treat the range of addictions differently, both in terms of their seriousness and the degree of censure that is brought to them. Generally, it is most condemning of drug addiction (except that of nicotine) and, in some cases, sex addiction, particularly where the target of the addiction is illegal, such as in child pornography. Addiction to shopping, junk-food and gambling tend to be treated rather light-heartedly, whereas society has little to say on the topic of addiction to exercise. The workaholic is often valued highly by employers and colleagues for his or her enterprise and dedication.

You might also speculate along the following lines. To some extent, the attitude of society depends upon whether harm is caused to others. For example, someone addicted to shopping who has a great deal of money and does not need to steal is less likely to incur censure than a shoplifter. A cigarette smoker might be tolerated except where passive smoking is involved.

Lethality

Activities such as gambling or sex cannot usually be *directly* lethal but the associated consequences can be lethal in various forms. For example, some activities by individuals addicted to sex run a high risk of violence and infection (Carnes, 2001). Also, many forms of addiction can be so destructive as to lead to suicide, following loss of family and job, etc.

1.3 Features of addictions

1.3.1 Pathways into addiction

An initial phase of prior engagement with an activity is, of course, necessary in order to become addicted to it. There are many reasons why people engage in an addictive activity in the first place, including psychological, social and biological reasons.

Activity 1.2 Initiation of addictive activities

(LO 1.3) Allow 5 minutes

Think about reports in the popular media as to why people first start activities that have the potential to become addictive. You might like to reflect on your own experiences and those of friends. Make a short list of the factors involved.

Two closely related questions are:

- Why would someone initiate a potentially addictive activity in the first place?
- Is there anything about the circumstances of initiation and early engagement with the activity that predict a later tendency for it to become addictive?

There are a number of studies investigating the first question. For example, studies in the USA, on alcohol, nicotine and cannabis, show that the social contribution of peer association and pressure is a major factor triggering the first taking of the substance, as is family conflict (Brook et al., 2010; Kobus and Henry, 2010). Research in Spain reveals that peer association and use of legal drugs were predictors of initiation of cannabis use in young people, as was 'having nothing else to do' (Pérez et al., 2010). Of course, the opposite side of the same coin consists of protective factors, so it is useful to look at those young people who do *not* engage in drug-taking. In young African-American males, evidence suggests that family coherence and a strong sense of ethnic identity could offer protection (Brook et al., 2010). In terms of a biopsychosocial perspective, these reasons perhaps most clearly illustrate the social dimension, and were emphasised by Vic in the case of smoking.

Again emphasising the relevance of a biopsychosocial perspective, in some cases, addictive activity starts as a result of *biological* changes within the body. An example of this is people with Parkinson's disease taking dopamine agonists as a treatment. These boost dopaminergic activity in certain brain pathways that are not the intended targets of the medicine, which sometimes leads to addictions to gambling and sex (Lim et al., 2008). The importance of dopamine for addiction is discussed in the next chapter.

The meaning of the term 'agonist' is given in Book 1, Section 2.4.2.

Moving on now to the second of the questions posed above. Some people cope well while engaging in activities that have the potential to become addictive and do not become addicted. Of course, for example, not every drinker of alcohol becomes addicted to it; neither does everyone who performs sexual behaviour become addicted to sex. As with alcohol, there are 'social users' of heroin and cocaine. Exactly why some people become addicted and others do not depends upon several factors, some of which are described in this section (more in Chapter 3). A good starting point is the fact that behaviour of any kind always occurs within a context and this can give important clues as to the factors underlying behaviour and when it becomes addictive. For example, taking a drug, going to a casino, or engaging in any other potentially addictive activity, occurs within a certain *psychological context* of the individual's mood of, say, elation, depression, anxiety or stress. It also takes place within a broader environment that has both physical and social properties. Gambling or taking drugs might occur when the person is alone or within a group of other individuals who are similarly motivated.

Social context

It appears that most research on context and addiction has taken place in the case of drug use but some of the same principles apply throughout the range of addictions. One of the clearest and most important messages in the study of drug addiction is summarised below.

Although the chemical properties of drugs are important to addiction, the answer to why people take drugs cannot be found simply by *studying these properties*. For example, if the individual has a supportive context with rich social opportunities, the risk of drug addiction is much lower than for people in a psychological vacuum and experiencing lack of social support (Alexander, 2008; Peele and Degrandpre, 1998). Some spiral out of control within a drug culture that shapes all aspects of their life, involving, for example, prostitution in order to pay for drugs (Fast et al., 2010).

It seems then that, particularly in the case of drugs such as cocaine and heroin, as well as alcohol, people become addicted mainly as a response to **social dislocation** (Alexander, 2000, 2008). This term refers to the loss of identity as an integrated member of a community that offers nurture and support. At an individual level, people are more likely to become addicted if they lose integration: for example, with unemployment and family breakdown. Historical records suggest that dislocation of Native Canadian populations was soon followed by a massive rise in alcohol addiction (Alexander, 2000). As another example from Canada, comparing across groups, Vancouver has a particularly high frequency of both socially displaced people and addiction to cocaine and heroin (Alexander, 2000). Most people living in Vancouver were born elsewhere. The statistics on addiction are based upon such indices as death rates from alcoholism and drug overdose, arrests for drug use and self-reports of drug use. These are, of course, far from perfect measures but are strongly suggestive that stress (Book 2) is a major factor in addiction. Consideration of the answer to the two questions posed above would suggest the value of a biopsychosocial perspective on addiction.

A study of a population of Native Americans in the USA, found that the younger the age of initiation into substance use, the greater was the later risk of developing addiction (Whitesell et al., 2009). Moreover, if the early initiation was associated with a particular social context of adversity, such as violent parental discord or childhood abuse, this appeared to increase the chances of later addiction (Klanecky et al., 2009). How can this be explained? Multiple factors are probably involved. Finding a solution to early psychological distress is one possibility. Fitting into a social network of other heavy users is another (Fast et al., 2010). In the case of alcohol and considering a German sample, Buchmann et al. (2009) speculated that early exposure might have caused changes to the developing brain such as to increase later vulnerability to addiction – a biological factor. Indeed, it is now commonly accepted that changes may occur within the brain as a result of engaging in addictive activity such as to make it more likely to be repeated – a biological factor (Robinson and Berridge, 1993), and one that is discussed in more detail in Chapter 3.

Therefore the environmental context and psychological events associated with the arrival of the drug in the body are also of crucial importance and must be considered along with any biological effects, which again points to the relevance of a biopsychosocial model (Peele and Degrandpre, 1998).

A so-called animal model can provide some insight here. One experiment investigated the role of social context on the intake of opiate drugs by rats. Some rats were housed in a large and complex ('enriched') environment with social companions, whereas others were housed in individual cages (Alexander and Hadaway, 1982). The socially housed rats took only a tiny fraction of the amount of drug taken by the isolated rats. This might be a suitable animal model of the isolation and despair experienced by some humans addicted to drugs. It might model the protective effect of integration into society.

Events closely associated with the addictive behaviour

Obviously the arrival of a drug in the body is preceded by the acquisition of the drug: for example, purchase of cigarettes, visiting a drug dealer, pub or off-licence. Subsequently, it is closely associated in time with a particular 'vehicle of delivery' (e.g. a syringe, a pipe, a cigarette or a glass) and a particular action (such as puffing). In the brain, these events and actions form close links with the arrival of the chemical in the body and the whole complex must be understood in order to fully understand drug addiction (Stewart et al., 1984). Similarly, prior to the addictive activity, the person addicted to gambling or sex needs to find a suitable location (e.g. computer terminal, casino, red-light district).

A wealth of evidence suggests that classical conditioning (Book 1, Section 1.3.2) is a process involved in addictive activities. Some suggestive evidence derives from the study of rats. In humans, such stimuli as the sight of the drug or the full syringe or the feel of the smoke in the mouth and nose are neutral stimuli that become powerful conditional stimuli by virtue of their association with the arrival of the drug in the body (the unconditional stimulus) (Stewart et al., 1984). They acquire the capacity to trigger changes in the brain. Such conditioning appears to explain a peculiar phenomenon known as 'needle freak'. In one study, it was found that after some people had extensive experience with taking heroin, the quality of the heroin could be compromised with little effect on the high. In some cases, the 'drug' was diluted with inert material such that there was very little heroin left, yet still a high was obtained (Stewart et al., 1984).

Consider the person who is attempting to give up taking a drug. Baker et al. (2006) argued the need to consider two interrelated aspects of abstinence and the associated withdrawal effect: *pharmacological withdrawal* and *behavioural withdrawal*. In the case of cigarettes, pharmacological withdrawal refers to the effect of not having nicotine in the body, whereas behavioural withdrawal refers to the effect of no longer engaging in the mechanical act of lighting and drawing on the cigarette. The sight of other people lighting up or even the sight of cigarette advertisements might be expected to trigger the urge to engage in this action.

Some lowering of drug urges can be achieved by going through the drug-related ritual even in the absence of the chemical properties of the drug. For example, a limited suppression of nicotine urges is obtained from smoking nicotine-free cigarettes and some suppression of heroin urges follows injection of a mild saline (i.e. salt) solution (Baker et al., 2006; Stewart et al., 1984). Some treatments for addiction involve taking the chemical but in the absence of the normal self-administration ritual (e.g. the use of nicotine patches). Their limited efficacy might be in large part due to the fact that they do not answer the needs of behavioural withdrawal.

- What does this evidence suggest concerning the best way to try to treat nicotine addiction?

☐ It suggests the value of combining the use of nicotine-free cigarettes and nicotine patches.

Self-image, stress and mood

Drug-taking is more likely when the individual is in particular psychological states. For example, one study of cocaine users (Singer, 1993) found that use was particularly high at times of low self-esteem. This points to addictive activities as reflections of attempts at coping with problems.

Across a range of activities, stress exacerbates the tendency to engage in behaviours that either are already addictive or have the capacity to become addictive. Individuals addicted to drugs frequently relapse at times of high stress. Some individuals first find themselves attracted to 'illicit' sex at times of high stress, such as exams or job insecurity, with the sexual addiction appearing to be a coping strategy (Maltz and Maltz, 2008; Schneider and Weiss, 2001).

Several factors appear to be involved in the association between stress and addiction. One rather obvious one considered already is that the person learns that the addictive activity forms a means of escape from stress. The addictive activity occupies the mind with a strongly sought goal and thereby is a form of *self-medication* for distress.

An observation that is entirely compatible with this link between stress and addiction is that stress lowers the capacity to resist temptation (Tiffany, 1990). There is evidence that this capacity requires access to what is a limited resource of conscious processing by the brain (Baumeister et al., 2007). If such conscious processing is engaged with trying to solve other problems, the chances are that the addictive activity might not be resisted. One does not need to be an addicted person to observe a similar form of this effect. Surely all of us have been preoccupied with something and have made a careless mistake that goes against our conscious intentions.

A related observation is that the capacity to resist temptation shows some fatigue with use, by analogy with how muscles fatigue (Baumeister et al., 2007). So, having had to resist the first temptation of the day, this lowers the capacity to resist the subsequent temptation.

Explanation of another process by which stress can exacerbate the tendency to engage in addictive activities will need to wait until Chapter 3.

Tolerance

The term tolerance is normally used in connection with drug-taking, though it can be applied also to non-drug-related addictive activities. It refers to the fact that, in order to obtain a given effect of a drug, over time increased amounts of drug are needed. The body adapts to the presence of the drug and this tends to lead to an escalation in dose over time. A similar phenomenon is shown by individuals addicted to sex who tend to require increased levels of stimulation (e.g. increased risk) in order to obtain the same degree of high (Moskowitz and Roloff, 2007).

Withdrawal

After having experienced the consequences of an addictive behaviour, people then develop expectations of achieving them again in the future. The consequence is usually one of improving the psychological state (e.g. achieving euphoria or at least lifting depression or anxiety), so they might well be motivated to try again. The flip side of this is that even with a relatively low rate of initial exposure to nicotine (e.g. one cigarette per day), young people can experience irritability and loss of control when not smoking, which appears to contribute to addiction to nicotine. Newcomers to cigarette smoking often underestimate the extent to which even very limited dabbling in the habit can lead to loss of control (Rose et al., 2010).

It should be noted that there is controversy over the importance of withdrawal symptoms in triggering urges and addictive activity, including relapse, amongst those trying to quit. In certain addictions (e.g. to heroin), the characteristic bodily manifestations of withdrawal are not invariably related to urges and the motivation to resume drug-taking (Alexander and Schweighofer, 1988; Robinson and Berridge, 1993). This led Robinson and Berridge to suggest that memories of the 'high' and cues associated with obtaining a 'high' in the past are what triggers relapse. Perhaps the safest assumption is that both painful withdrawal symptoms and memories of earlier 'highs' play a role.

Some authors have taken the expression 'withdrawal symptoms' to mean those symptoms that are observable in the body such as shaking and sweating. However, this ignores the powerful effects on *mood* that follow cessation of an addictive activity. Across different types of addictive drugs, what seems to be a more common factor of withdrawal and the motivation to resume is the experience of *negative affect* (Baker et al., 2006). Negative affect is characterised by such terms as 'irritable', 'depressed', 'stressed' and 'anxious'. Some addicted individuals report that the state of withdrawal is comparable to the loss of close social relationships or separation. In many cases, repeated resumption of the addictive activity when in a state of negative affect leads to an expectation that engaging in the activity is rapidly and very effectively followed by alleviation of negative affect (Baker et al., 2006).

It would appear that a similar mental state of negative affect and its alleviation frequently accompanies relapse in those addicted to non-drug-related activities (Cunningham-Williams et al., 2009). This common feature points to the value of the generic term 'addiction' to cover both drug-related and non-drug-related activities. It points to the *psychological* dimension in any addictive activity.

Pain

People suffering from serious pain are sometimes administered the drug morphine. It used to be believed that there was a danger of morphine addiction, but this fear has been greatly exaggerated (Melzack, 1988). One study looked at thousands of Israeli casualties of the 1973 Yom Kippur War who received morphine (Melzack and Wall, 1996). It was found that none showed signs of addiction to the drug. That is to say, their desire for morphine and their use of the drug was specific to the context of pain. If their brains had changed as a result of the use of morphine, this was not sufficient to trigger drug-seeking *outside the context* of treatment for pain.

War and peace

In the Vietnam War, there was a ready supply of addictive drugs and a large number of US servicemen took heroin regularly. When peace came in 1975 and these men were returned to the USA, a public health emergency was feared with the belief that the war veterans would be forced onto the black market to obtain illicit drugs, and that this would be accompanied by a rise in violent crime (Robins et al., 1975). In fact, only a tiny percentage did resume the use of these drugs. In other words, for the vast majority, their drug habit was context-specific. Drugs were the solution to a problem when in a particularly stressful context. If the users' brains were changed by the presence of the drug, this change was not *sufficient* to trigger irresistible drug urges when the context was changed. Such examples illustrate once again the benefits of taking social context into account, as summarised in the term 'biopsychosocial perspective'.

1.3.2 What *is* and *is not* addictive

You have seen that a variety of behaviours and drugs can be addictive, but at the same time there are behaviours and drugs that are not addictive. Much of the research to date has focused on the difference between addictive and non-addictive drugs rather than behaviours so we will do the same and ask what is it about certain drugs that make them a risk for addiction?

Of course, this does not mean that psychoactive drugs which are not addictive are safe. The absence of addiction does not imply the absence of changes to underlying neural systems.

One suggestion is that a drug with psychoactive properties will be addictive. The term **psychoactive drug** refers to a class of drugs that are characterised by having effects on the brain, such that there is an alteration in the conscious mind ('mind-altering'). However, not all psychoactive drugs are addictive. For example, large numbers of young people take the drug ecstasy at raves and clubs but they do not become addicted to it. Similarly, magic mushrooms were legally on sale in Britain in the early part of the 21st century but there were no reports of addiction. It is almost certain that there were no accounts of street crime or burglary motivated by the need to obtain money to purchase magic mushrooms. Likewise, in the 1960s, there was a craze amongst some people to take the drug LSD for its mind-altering effects. However, there were no reports of LSD addiction or associated social and health problems. In contrast drugs such as heroin are associated with addiction and social problems as people addicted to them sometimes resort to house-breaking and street crime to obtain the money to buy them.

Likewise there are drugs that are apparently less strong psychoactively which are addictive. For example, despite the best efforts of the US tobacco industry lobby to claim otherwise, nicotine is highly addictive by several criteria, even though surely few would describe its effect as 'utterly mind-blowing'. So addictive is nicotine that in one survey, people who were under treatment for addiction to drugs like heroin were asked about quitting their nicotine habit (Kozlowski et al., 1989). Most reported that this would prove more difficult than quitting their other addiction.

So, some strongly psychoactive drugs meet none of the criteria of addiction, whereas others, that may be less psychoactive, are addictive. It is now accepted that rather than general 'psychoactive properties', it is the actions of the drugs specifically on the brain's dopaminergic systems which are thought to underlie their addictiveness, a topic discussed in Chapter 2.

1.3.3 Combined addictive activities

Some people have a single addiction but often addictions occur in combination. For example, some people addicted to sex are simultaneously addicted to alcohol or cocaine (Carnes, 2001; Washton and Stone-Washton, 1993), as indeed are some people addicted to gambling (Cunningham-Williams et al., 2009). In other cases, there might be a single addiction (e.g. gambling) but the person engages in a potentially addictive activity (e.g. taking cocaine) occasionally. Such combinations can give insights into the processes underlying addictive behaviour. Those with combined sex and cocaine addictions will sometimes plan ahead to generate a 'super-high': for example, by booking into a hotel room equipped with the drug and with access to 'adult movies' (Maltz and Maltz, 2008). In other cases, quite without planning ahead, engaging in the one activity can trigger an urge to engage in another. In part, this could reflect the role of classical conditioning, since the activities will have been paired in the past. (In Activity 1.1, Vic described the context of a good meal as a trigger to smoking.) Another likely reason for this association will be explored in the discussion of the brain mechanisms of addiction (Chapter 2).

1.3.4 Comparison of addiction with obsessive–compulsive disorder

Addictive behaviour is sometimes described as 'compulsive'. This might remind you of John's obsessive–compulsive hand-washing behaviour described in Book 1, Section 1.1.1. Often in the media the terms 'obsessive' and 'compulsive', either singly or as a compound, are used as synonyms for what is more correctly termed an 'addiction'. Interestingly, the converse does not occur: an obsessive–compulsive activity such as hand-washing or checking is rarely described as 'addictive'.

This overlap of terminology points to a striking common feature between obsessions and addictions.

- ■ Can you describe what it is?

- □ In both cases, what can be perfectly normal behaviour is taken to excess such that serious long-term consequences are suffered. In both cases, temporary peace is gained at the price of long-term harm.

Interestingly, one form of medication used for treating OCD, selective serotonin reuptake inhibitors (e.g. Prozac®) (Book 1, Section 2.4.1), is also used in the treatment of gambling and sexual addictions. It might owe its efficacy in each case by strengthening the capacity to resist the impulsive urges that demand immediate gratification.

In spite of the similarities, there is one fundamental distinction between addictions and OCD.

- ■ Can you spot what it is?

- □ At their roots, addictions are all based upon the gain of something that is usually described as 'positive', 'rewarding' and 'positively reinforcing' (e.g. food, sex, a 'high' or money), whereas OCD involves escape from something aversive (e.g. fear of contamination, anxiety about leaving a door unlocked).

The key expression here is 'at their roots'. In reality, after getting addicted, the behaviour might owe as much, if not more, to eliminating stress and/or negative effects of withdrawal as getting to euphoria (as in the case of Mary).

1.4 Investigating addiction: comparison with conventional behaviour

1.4.1 An evolutionary perspective

It is widely agreed that humans are the product of a long process of evolution. Evolution tends to yield a fit between an animal and its environment: for example, animals have evolved efficient means of gaining nutrients, repelling rivals, escaping from danger and finding mates. In such terms, addictions might be seen as *aberrations* since they appear to be to the long-term disadvantage of the person displaying the addiction.

Of course, addictions might also bring some long-term benefits: for example, individuals addicted to drugs may find themselves in a community of like-minded and non-judgemental individuals.

Therefore, it seems that animals could not have evolved *special* processes that serve the role of producing addictions. So, it must be assumed that addictions are the product of abnormal functioning within processes that underlie conventional behaviour. A glance at how such processes produce normal behaviour and a comparison with addictive activities might provide insights. Of primary importance in understanding addictions is the role of classical conditioning, which was mentioned in the previous section. The present section considers the role of conditioning in non-drug-related activities in non-humans and how this might give insights into human addictive activities.

1.4.2 The study of non-human species

Understanding has been gained by the study of the behaviour of non-human species, as simplified models of the human condition (as noted already for rats in enriched environments). Using, for example, rats, conventional behaviours can be compared with drug-taking, albeit under contrived conditions. Of course, non-humans cannot speak and therefore do not permit the subjective nature of experience to be explored. Researchers are confined to the objective study of their brains and behaviour.

The expression **motivation** is used to refer to the strength and direction that behaviour takes and it can be measured in a number of ways. A piece of equipment that can be used is known as the **Skinner box** (Figure 1.4). The name derives from its inventor, the American psychologist, Burrhus F. Skinner (Book 2, Section 4.1.2).

Traditionally, a hungry rat is trained to press a lever to obtain a small pellet of food. After training, the animal reliably presses the lever to earn food. A measure of the strength of its motivation, which in this case is food-directed, is the frequency or force with which it presses the lever. Similarly, a thirsty rat can be trained to earn the reward of water. Of particular interest here is the observation that rats can be trained to earn small portions of some of those drugs that are addictive to humans. The drug is normally injected into the blood through a permanently implanted tube in response to a lever-press. The Skinner box is a possible animal model of certain features of human addictions. However, note that it is an unnatural environment devoid of social contact and hence might model human drug intake under only comparably deprived conditions (Peele and Degrandpre, 1998).

Figure 1.4 Skinner box for a rat.

Suppose that, in stage 1 of an experiment, a tone or a light is paired with a reward (food or a drug) earned by lever-pressing (Figure 1.5). In stage 2, the rat is put in what is known as 'extinction conditions'. This means that, when the rat presses the lever, food or drug no longer follows. After a period of time, the rat will stop responding. However, presentation of the tone or light is sufficient to trigger the rat to move over to the lever and start pressing again (stage 3). This experiment is an example of a combination of instrumental and classical conditioning (Book 1, Section 1.3.2).

■ What is the aspect that represents classical conditioning?

□ Pairing of the light or the tone with drug or food in stage 1.

■ In these terms, what is the neutral stimulus?

□ The tone or light prior to its pairing with the reward.

■ To what does the term 'conditional stimulus' refer?

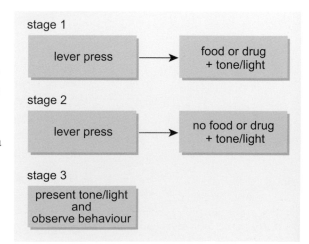

Figure 1.5 Experimental protocol for measuring motivation using the Skinner box.

□   The tone or light after repeated pairing with the food or drug.

■   What is the feature described by the term 'instrumental conditioning'?

□   Lever-pressing is followed by the reinforcement of food or drug, such that lever-pressing increases in frequency.

This experiment would appear to model some of the power of conditional stimuli to trigger relapse in humans. Examples include the sight of other addicted individuals or the sound of the computer and the feel of the mouse for those addicted to online pornography (Putnam, 2000). Patrick in Activity 1.1 described the pull exerted by the sights and sounds of the betting shop.

Reward needs to be immediate in the Skinner box for learning to occur. Rats are not good at delayed gratification and you might well know some humans who are similar! Delayed consequences are relatively ineffective as controls of behaviour, which seems to model a feature of addiction.

Once a rat is trained to lever-press, it can be put on what is termed a **partial reinforcement schedule**. This means that only, say, on average every 10th lever-press earns the reward. Once 'stretched' in this way, rats persist long and hard with lever-pressing, even when no reward follows. Have a look back at the range of addictions shown in Table 1.2.

■   A partial reinforcement schedule seems to model which of them particularly well?

□   Gambling. The Skinner box is something like a fruit machine and the laboratory can be turned into a miniature Las Vegas. The person addicted to internet sex also seems to fit this model since such an individual is never sure when they will find the ideal image.

Rats also exhibit bodily symptoms of withdrawal when the supply of a drug is terminated. These symptoms appear to be something like the human equivalents. If the drug supply is terminated, the rat will increase the rate at which it presses the lever. This can be taken as analogous to the human experience of craving for a drug in its absence, though of course rat studies are dealing only with the behavioural expression of craving as a possible index of the subjective psychological state.

1.4.3   Generalisation to humans

Non-drug-related activities

Insights can be gained into addictions and their basis in the brain by the simple consideration that some addictions appear to be *gross exaggerations* of what is normal behaviour. Consider, for example, sexual behaviour or feeding. Both of these behaviours are, of course, perfectly normal in the sense of the array of activities in which humans engage. When these behaviours get 'out of control', logically, it is not necessary to postulate that completely distinct processes underlie the deviant form. Rather, it would seem that normal controls have got out of kilter. For example, our motivational systems of feeding evolved in an environment very different from that of the supermarket abundance that surrounds people living in affluent societies these days. Excessive eating of junk food to the point of addiction appears to reflect an imbalance between motivational signals that excite behaviour and those that offer restraint on behaviour. A similar logic could be applied to sexual addiction in that commercial sex, as available online offers an array of possibilities that were not around when humans evolved. Our ancestors were only able to survive by their success at gaining resources. One can speculate that shopping and gambling addictions are reflections of brain processes that underlie the acquisition of resources, a desire that is rather widespread in consumer societies!

Drug-related activities

Drugs cannot be fitted quite so neatly as other addictive activities into an evolutionary pattern but a further leap of the imagination can easily accommodate them. Think what was required for an animal, human or otherwise, to survive. It needs to be motivated by the detection of such things as food, water and mates. When, for example, it is depleted of nutrients, it needs to be drawn particularly to sources of food. Animals such as dogs, rats and humans are equipped with processes of reward and reinforcement (Book 1, Section 1.3.2) for engaging in such activities. This will encourage the animal to repeat these activities in future when it is in a state of nutrient deficiency. As you will learn in Chapter 2, drugs appear to tap into these same processes of reward and reinforcement and to powerfully excite them, such that a rat will press a lever to obtain drugs (Nesse and Berridge, 1997). By analogy, a person obtains a high of pleasure and is persuaded to repeat the behaviour in the future.

1.5 Final word

This chapter has introduced a range of activities that appear to meet the criteria of addiction as defined by DSM-IV-TR. By now you should have a feel for the difficulties and ambiguities associated with trying to define what the term 'addiction' means exactly. This is perhaps inevitable where any definition is likely to rely in part upon the subjective evidence of the person with the addiction and trying to fit this to objective evidence on such things as activity in particular brain regions and levels of neurotransmitters (Chapter 2).

Of course, one should not deny that there are some real differences between addictions: for example, the person addicted to shopping will experience withdrawal that is rather different from the physical bodily symptoms of alcohol or heroin withdrawal. Amongst the various forms of addiction, people addicted to drugs such as heroin and cocaine appear to be most likely to resort to crime to fuel their habit, though not all do so and some people addicted to, say, gambling steal to maintain their behaviour. Hopefully, you will agree that some common features emerge across addictions, which justifies investigating and describing them under the same heading. This approach also suggests the value of looking for common underlying processes in the brain, to which the discussion turns next.

1.6 Summary of Chapter 1

- The ICD-10 and DSM-IV-TR specify a number of criteria for defining substance dependence, a term with some similarity in meaning to substance 'addiction'. However, not all 'dependence' would be said to be 'addictive'. The term 'addiction' is still controversial. However, here the term is used to include the DSM criteria for substance use, whilst also encompassing addiction to non-substance-based activities.

- It is possible to adapt these criteria to define a number of non-drug-related activities as addictions, such as excessive consumption of junk foods, gambling and work.

- A possible defining feature of addiction is where an activity is taken to excess such that it has a harmful effect on the addicted person and possibly also those closest to him or her.

- Addictions are such that engaging in the addictive activity brings immediate subjective benefits but with actual or possible long-term costs.

- An element of risk is involved in some addictive activities and might increase the attraction of the activity.

- A number of features may underlie initial engagement with addictive activities; in particular, social dislocation.

- A common feature of withdrawal across a number of activities is negative affect.

- Contextual factors, such as stress, social context and external events associated with the addictive activity, play a key role in addiction.

- Classical conditioning occurs between an addictive activity and associated events.

- Addictions sometimes occur in combinations.

- A comparison of addiction and OCD reveals the similarity of control by short-term gain in the face of long-term negative consequences.

- Addictions can be viewed as the abnormal functioning of controls that evolved to serve normal behaviour and they can be investigated in simple settings such as using a rat trained in a Skinner box to press a lever for the reward of a drug.

1.7 Learning outcomes

LO 1.1 Show that you understand that addiction refers to a range of activities, not all of which involve substance use. (KU1)

LO 1.2 Describe the defining characteristic of addiction as compulsive use of a substance or performance of a behaviour despite long-term negative consequences. Give examples of a range of addictions and be able to justify their inclusion as addictive activities. (KU1, CS2, CS4)

LO 1.3 Describe some of the factors that might underlie initial engagement with an addictive substance or behaviour and the context in which addiction takes place. (KU1, KU4, CS4)

LO 1.4 Describe some of the biological, psychological and social factors that underlie addictions. Explain the ways in which a biopsychosocial model is relevant to understanding addiction. (KU1, KU3, CS3)

LO 1.5 Distinguish between the direct and indirect effects of addiction on health. (KU3, CS3)

LO1.6 Show that you recognise that addiction can affect more than the addicted individual and can have wide-ranging social, health and financial implications. (KU3, CS5)

1.8 Self-assessment questions

SAQ 1.1 (LOs 1.1, 1.2 and 1.6)

By adapting the DSM-IV-TR criteria for substance abuse, which of the seven does gambling fit?

SAQ 1.2 (LOs 1.3 and 1.5)

What would be meant by claiming that the dangers of engaging in addictive activities are, in part, 'hypothetical'?

SAQ 1.3 (LO 1.4)

If the phenomenon termed 'needle freak' can be explained, at least in part, in terms of classical conditioning, what would constitute (i) the unconditional stimulus, (ii) the unconditional response, (iii) the conditional stimulus and (iv) the conditional response?

SAQ 1.4 (LO 1.2)

Addictive behaviour is sometimes described as 'compulsive'. Why would a diagnosis of OCD not be appropriate for addictive behaviour?

SAQ 1.5 (LOs 1.3 and 1.4)

Suppose that a person remains drug-free until coming into an environment previously associated with drug-taking, at which point they relapse. In terms of classical conditioning, what term would be applied to the environment?

Chapter 2 Hijacking motivation: the biology of addiction

Eleanor Dommett

2.1 Introduction

In the previous chapter and in Activity 1.1, you were introduced to a number of people living with addiction. You saw that some addictions, such as Mary's heroin addiction, were considered particularly unacceptable by society, whilst others, such as the workaholism shown by Bryan, may be considered a positive character attribute. Irrespective of the actual object of the addiction, be it heroin, nicotine, gambling or work, you saw that the addiction did not develop overnight, but rather the behaviour became gradually more compulsive, until it continued despite negative consequences.

In this chapter, you will learn about the biological changes that occur in the brain in response to the objects of addiction. Through this knowledge you will learn how certain drugs and behaviours can be distinguished as addictive or non-addictive, providing a biological dimension that can be factored into the biopsychosocial framework of addiction. Before we examine the effects of these addictive behaviours and drugs, however, we first need to consider the normal processes that underlie why behaviour of any kind might be performed at all. To answer this question we need to look at the biological basis of motivation.

2.2 Motivation: driving our behaviour

The term motivation is used in all sorts of situations. For example, you may have referred to people as being motivated to work or motivated by money. But in the context of specific behaviours, when the term motivation is used it is normally referring to specific conditions which underlie someone performing a particular behaviour. For example, hunger might motivate a person to seek out and eat food, or thirst would motivate an individual to seek out water to satisfy their need. Motivation, therefore, can be the difference between an action being considered and an action actually being performed. In the case of addiction, the actions become performed repeatedly and at the cost of other actions. So in order to understand addiction you must first understand motivation. To begin to understand motivation, a number of important definitions are required.

In psychology, any goal to which behaviour is directed can be considered a reward: for example, food or a sexual partner can be considered the goal for particular behaviours. However, it is important to recognise that rewards, which are considered to be something desirable, are not the only things that motivate behaviour. Indeed, you may recall from Section 1.3.1 of Book 1 that people may behave in a certain way to avoid an aversive outcome, such as John who has OCD. As such, the term reward is too narrow for our purposes and therefore we shall use the term **incentive** which better represents the wide-ranging nature of goals of behaviour.

These incentives are often the focus of two different types of learning with which you are already familiar: classical conditioning and instrumental conditioning (Book 1, Section 1.3.2). As you have come across these before, only a brief recap will be given here. Classical conditioning is the term given to the process by which a neutral stimulus becomes associated with an unconditional stimulus such as an incentive and, through this association becomes capable of eliciting a response normally reserved for the unconditional stimulus and is thereafter referred to as the conditional stimulus. The most well-known example of this was demonstrated by Ivan Pavlov when he found that repeatedly pairing presentation of food with the sound of a bell to a dog eventually resulted in the dog salivating in response to the sound of the bell alone.

The second type of learning, instrumental conditioning, requires the person or non-human animal to be *instrumental*, or play an active role, in the learning process, unlike classical conditioning where the changes occur passively, merely through repeated exposure. Instrumental conditioning can be studied using both rewards and punishments as incentives. Psychologists use the Skinner box (Figure 1.4) to examine how animals will work to reach an incentive: for example, pressing a lever to gain a food pellet or prevent a small electric shock.

From these experiments, psychologists concluded that such incentives can act as **reinforcers**, meaning that they will increase the probability of the behaviour that preceded their presentation being repeated in the future; the behaviour is said to be reinforced. Where the behaviour results in receipt of something desirable, it is called **positive reinforcement** and will have the effect of increasing the likelihood of repeating the behaviour that led to it. Alternatively, where the behaviour results in the removal of an aversive stimulus, the behaviour is still reinforced, meaning that the chances of repetition increase, but this time it is termed **negative reinforcement**.

In terms of observable behaviour, motivation can be divided into two separate phases: **appetitive** and **consummatory**. The appetitive phase refers to the actions that are likely to lead to presentation of the incentive: for example, preparation of food or seeking out a sexual partner. The consummatory phase refers to engagement with the incentive, such as eating the food or engaging in sexual activity.

In attempting to identify the biological basis for motivation, it is important to recognise that behaviour involves a variety of different elements, and activation in the brain associated with motivation will need to be distinguished from other causes of activation in the brain.

■ Can you think what these other causes of activation might be?

☐ The brain is constantly processing sensory information and, in addition to this, any behaviour is likely to involve movement of some kind and this too will result in activation of different regions of the brain.

Although the brain is involved with many different tasks at any one time, it is possible to identify regions that have a specific role in motivation. This can be done because particular structures or groups of neurons will be especially active when the animal or person is engaged in a highly motivated behaviour: for example, lever-pressing for food (in the case of the rat in a Skinner box), or a person running to catch a bus.

- Can you think what sort of outcome you would look for in a test to determine whether a particular brain region is involved in the appetitive or consummatory phases of motivation?

- ☐ To identify regions involved in the appetitive phase you would look for regions that were preferentially active in the phase when the non-human animal or person was working towards the incentive (e.g. pressing the lever, running for the bus). By contrast, you would look for regions that were preferentially active in the brain during consumption of the incentive (e.g. eating the food pellet, reaching the bus) to identify regions important for the consummatory phase.

The demonstration that two different brain regions are active during the two different phases of motivation, where one region is active during the first phase and not the second, whilst the other region is active during the second phase but not the first, is referred to as **double dissociation**. As well as being able to look for this double dissociation in activity of brain regions, it is also possible to examine which parts of the brain impair motivation when they are damaged or removed. This is the basis of **lesion studies**. These are conducted in animals and involve a particular region of the brain being damaged or removed and the changes in behaviour that result being used to infer the function of that region. In some cases, psychologists may be able to learn from brain lesions in humans, such as those caused through accidental damage to the brain or illness. These are less controlled than induced lesions in non-human animals, with damage usually not being limited to the region of interest; however, if considered alongside other types of experiments, they can provide useful information. For example, damage to or removal of one region may impair the appetitive phase whilst damage to or removal of another may impair the consummatory phase.

- Can you think of a problem with this experimental design?

- ☐ The lesion study design assumes that information can be learnt about the function of a structure by damaging or removing it. An analogy is often drawn here with a computer – would you learn what the hard drive does by removing it and seeing what functions the computer can no longer perform? It is possible that you would glean some information about the function but it would be important to remember that the system under investigation is in an abnormal state (i.e. damaged).

It is important therefore to note that researchers are limited in their knowledge by the methods of investigation available to them. This is why it is prudent not to rely too heavily on conclusions from a study using just one type of method.

Using a combination of techniques, three important regions for motivation have now been identified: the **ventral tegmental area (VTA)**, the **nucleus accumbens (NAc)** and the **prefrontal cortex (PFC)**. These regions are shown in Figure 2.1. Take a few minutes to study this figure and orient yourself to looking at the brain.

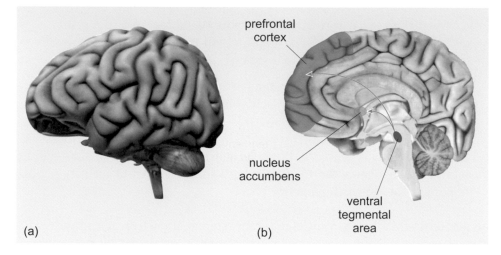

Figure 2.1 (a) An external view of the brain, most of which is covered by the highly folded cortex. In this image the person would be looking towards the left. (b) A cross-section of the same brain revealing the regions underneath the cortex.

A neuron that releases dopamine is referred to as a dopaminergic neuron.

Researchers have shown that two large connections between these regions are important in motivation. The first is the connection between the VTA and the NAc which is termed the mesolimbic pathway. This pathway is made up of neurons containing the neurotransmitter dopamine. The dopaminergic neurons extend their axons from the VTA to the NAc. The second connection that is important for motivation is between the VTA and the PFC. This connection is called the mesocortical pathway and also contains dopaminergic neurons. These two pathways are often grouped together and referred to collectively as the **mesolimbocortical pathway**.

Much of the research into motivation has been conducted in non-human animals, particularly rats. One of the reasons this is possible is because the same brain regions and the connections between them exist in the rat as they do in people. This is illustrated schematically in Figure 2.2, with the rat brain and motivation pathways shown below the human brain and pathways.

■ From the perspective of scientific research, what is the advantage of the similarity of this pathway in the rat and human brains?

☐ The similarities mean that information gleaned about the function of the pathway in rats may give information as to how it functions in humans.

■ Why might it be useful, where addiction is concerned, to be able to investigate some of the properties in non-human animals?

☐ It would be unethical to expose a human to an addictive drug and risk them becoming addicted.

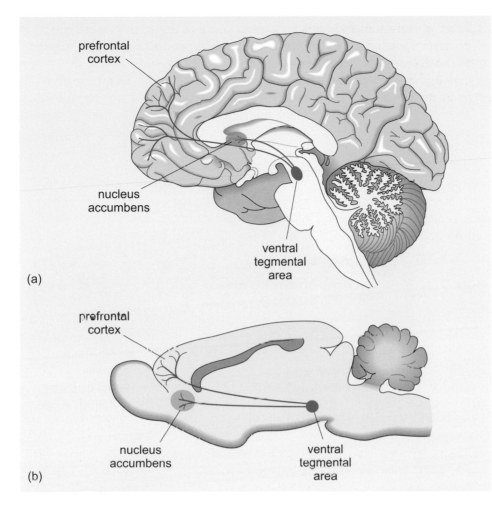

Figure 2.2   There are similarities between the motivation pathways in the human brain (a) and rat brain (b). In both instances the brain is facing towards the left.

One way to study humans but avoid the ethical concerns of causing an addiction is to work with people who are already addicted; however, this is not without its problems. For example, people may not be willing to admit to being addicted to a particular behaviour or drug, especially those that are considered less socially acceptable. As a result, data may not be reliable. Moreover, you learnt in Section 1.3.3 that individuals may combine use of more than one addictive drug or behaviour, and therefore it would be difficult to isolate the effects of individual drugs or behaviours in such people.

A further problem could arise from the fact that it is difficult to isolate particular variables in an already addicted population. For example, if you wished to look at the effects of heroin on a particular measure in people, it might be difficult to isolate this from the effects of other lifestyle choices that often accompany heroin use. Studies using non-human animals allow tightly controlled experiments to be conducted, which can reduce these problems with interpretation.

■   What drawbacks are there to studying addiction in non-human animals?

☐ When using an animal such as a rat, subjective experience must be inferred from behaviour and only certain behaviours can be investigated in rodents as their behavioural repertoire is not as wide as that of humans. In addition, some of the social influences and factors such as finances that may affect human behaviour are largely, if not completely, absent in animals. Thus, animal studies may limit us to a more biological perspective rather than a biopsychosocial one.

In order to investigate which phase of motivation (appetitive or consummatory) the mesolimbocortical pathway is important in, Pfaus et al. (1990) measured dopamine levels in both anticipation of (appetitive) and during (consummatory) sexual activity in male rats (see Box 2.1 for more detail on how this was done).

Box 2.1 Measuring dopamine levels using microdialysis

Microdialysis is a technique that allows experimenters to sample the chemicals within the brain in an awake, behaving animal. This is done by implanting two very fine tubes, one inside the other, into the brain as shown in the diagram. As Figure 2.3 shows, the inner tube of the microdialysis probe carries a salt solution, similar to that found naturally in the nervous system, into the brain (blue circles) whilst the outer tube of the probe removes the natural salt solution from the brain (yellow circles).

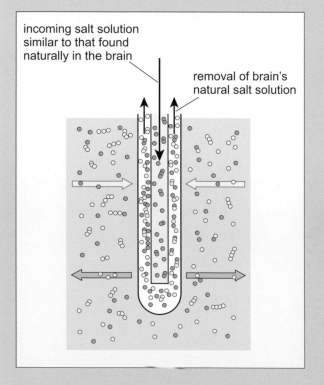

Figure 2.3 Membrane region of a microdialysis probe showing tubes for incoming and outgoing solutions.

At the tip of both tubes there is a special membrane called a dialysis membrane. This membrane allows some of the chemicals within the brain to move into the tubes and the salt solution to move out of the tubes. Therefore, when the solution is removed from the brain it will contain some of the chemicals that were in the brain, which may then be identified.

As a way to measure anticipation, they placed a female rat within sight of, but not accessible to, the male rat. After a brief period, the partition between the two animals was removed and sexual activity commenced. The experimenters recorded the amount of dopamine released in the nucleus accumbens throughout, and the results are shown in Figure 2.4. As a control, they also measured dopamine release when the female was not present, as shown in the 'male only' condition in Figure 2.4.

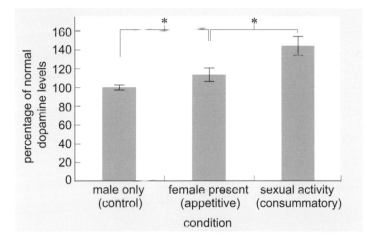

Figure 2.4 Dopamine levels recorded by microdialysis during the different phases of motivation. The 'male only' condition is used as a control condition to give an indication of baseline dopamine levels. * denotes that the change is statistically significant (Book 2, Section 1.3.5).

- From Figure 2.4, what is the difference between the level of dopamine in the 'male only' condition and the condition where the female is present?

- There is an increase of just over 10% when the female is present.

- From Figure 2.4, what is the difference between the level of dopamine in the condition where the female is present and where sexual activity occurs?

- There is an increase of about 30% when sexual activity occurs.

These data suggest that dopamine levels increased significantly during the appetitive phase and consummatory phase of motivation. However, a follow-on study by Pfaus and Philips (1991) showed that dopamine antagonists, i.e. a drug which blocks the effects of dopamine disrupted appetitive behaviours far more than consummatory ones. This suggests that dopamine levels in the synapse are related to the pursuit of a goal (the appetitive phase), in this case a sexual partner, over and above the consummatory phase, in this instance sexual activity. This is also supported by findings where dopamine levels have been depleted: for example, with a lesion to the region containing the dopaminergic neurons. When this happens, there is a loss of appetitive behaviour, such as that directed towards a sexual partner.

The mesolimbocortical pathway, therefore, is thought to be fundamental to the appetitive (i.e. the seeking and, in humans, 'wanting') aspect of motivation. Thus, this pathway is described as being responsible for **incentive motivation**. Moreover, activation of this pathway by a stimulus is associated with an increase in the incentive pull or wanting for that stimulus, such that it might then be pursued with more vigour. Normally this pathway is activated by natural incentives such as food and sex, but as you will see shortly it can also be activated by other objects of addiction.

What then underlies the consummatory phase of motivation, also termed the 'liking' element? One way to test this is to use the taste-reactivity test, in which small amounts of food are placed on the tongues of rats and their reactions watched. This eliminates the appetitive behaviour which is related to dopamine levels. Substances that are described by humans as hedonically positive or pleasurable and liked trigger acceptance behaviours, whilst those deemed unpleasant trigger rejection reactions (see Figure 2.5).

Figure 2.5 (a) Taste acceptance reactions of rats to attractive substances. (b) Taste rejection reactions to aversive substances. Arrows indicate the sweep of the rat's head movement.

To refresh your memory of how agonists and antagonists work and what opioids are, return to Book 1, Section 2.4.2.

Using this test, researchers found that injection of dopamine agonists and antagonists had no effect on the reactions observed, leading them to conclude that dopamine did not underlie the pleasantness or liking of a stimulus. Instead they found that manipulating opioid receptor binding through use of antagonists and agonists could alter the reactions, with agonists producing more acceptance reactions and antagonists producing more rejection reactions. The researchers therefore concluded that the wanting (appetitive) aspect of motivation and the liking (consummatory) aspect are controlled by two different chemicals, dopamine and opioids, respectively.

Interestingly, however, as researchers turned their attention to stimuli that seem to command an abnormally high level of motivation, such as those that are the subject of addictions, the focus has significantly narrowed to consider the wanting element of motivation mediated by dopamine, rather than the liking aspect mediated by opioids. Focusing on dopamine does mean that researchers know less about why an individual might like a drug (for example) in contrast to why they want it. One reason for this focus is because those who have an addiction often report that their liking for the object of the addiction (e.g. heroin) is reduced or unchanged, whilst their wanting for it is increased. The next section therefore examines how these drugs and behaviours can affect the incentive motivation pathway.

2.3 Dopamine: the common factor?

You have seen that there is a wide range of drugs and behaviours that can become addictive. However, there is a surprising neurobiological similarity in their immediate effects in the brain, which may explain how they all act to reinforce the relevant behaviours such that their use or engagement is repeated. To learn more about these neurobiological mechanisms, we have to return to the ideas detailed in Book 1 about neurotransmission and the synapse.

2.3.1 Neurotransmission – the dopamine synapse

You will recall that neurons can communicate with each other by releasing specific neurotransmitters into the synaptic gap, between two neurons. Once the neurotransmitter has been released, it can bind to specific receptors on the neighbouring or postsynaptic neuron. This causes small electrical changes in the postsynaptic neuron, which when combined, determine whether the neuron will fire an action potential or not. Importantly, the activity of the neurotransmitter at the synapse cannot continue indefinitely, as you saw in Book 1 (Section 2.3.2).

■   There are two main methods of removing the neurotransmitter from the synapse. Can you remember what they are?

☐   Neurotransmitter can be removed by being broken down into its components by enzymes. Alternatively the neurotransmitter can be taken back into the neuron from which it was released via reuptake channels (Book 1, Figure 2.23).

Figure 2.6 indicates that the neurotransmitter binding to the receptor has an excitatory effect on the postsynaptic neuron and indeed this can be the case. However, remember that this is not always the case; in some instances, binding of a transmitter can have an inhibitory effect on the postsynaptic neuron so that it becomes less likely to produce an action potential. You might like to revisit Activity 2.2 in Book 1 to remind yourself of this in more detail before you move on.

Armed with this knowledge of neurotransmission and your understanding of the basic neurobiology of motivation, you can start to examine the shared

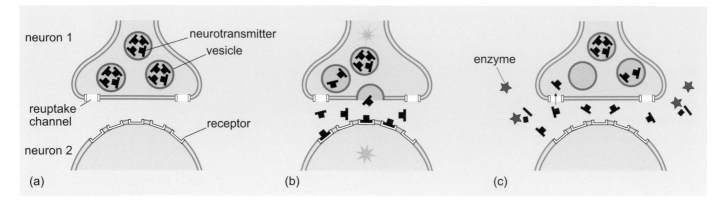

Figure 2.6 (a) A schematic synapse between the presynaptic neuron 1 and the postsynaptic neuron 2. (b) The arrival of an action potential at an axon terminal of neuron 1 triggers the release of the neurotransmitter. The neurotransmitter moves across the synapse and binds to specialised receptors on the postsynaptic neuron 2. This binding can be equated to a key fitting into a lock and results in electrical changes occurring in neuron 2 – hence the electrical signal can continue. It should be noted that some neurotransmitters will cause an excitatory effect and others an inhibitory effect. (c) Once in the synaptic gap, the neurotransmitter must be removed to ensure that neuron 2 receives a signal that reflects dynamic events. This can be through breakdown of the neurotransmitter into its component parts by enzymes or by reuptake into the neuron from which it was released (neuron 1), for later re-use.

mechanisms of action of the behaviours and drugs that can become addictive. Following over 30 years of research, it is now widely accepted that all addictive drugs, ranging from nicotine and cannabis to heroin and cocaine, act to increase levels of dopamine at the synapse. The exact mechanism of action of each drug varies but the result is always the same: increased dopamine levels at the synapse.

■ From what you know about the processes that take place at the synapse, list the different ways in which the synaptic levels of the neurotransmitter dopamine could be increased. (*Hint*: look at parts (b) and (c) of Figure 2.6.)

□ Synaptic levels of dopamine could be increased by: (i) increased dopamine release; (ii) decreased dopamine reuptake; or (iii) decreased dopamine breakdown.

2.3.2 Dopamine and addictive drugs

Different addictive drugs act in slightly different ways to increase the amount of dopamine at the synapse. Because cocaine works in a reasonably straightforward fashion to increase dopamine levels, this drug will be considered first. Cocaine acts to prevent dopamine being removed from the synapse by blocking the normal reuptake process. This is shown schematically in Figure 2.7, and in a brain scan of someone who has been given cocaine in Figure 2.8. For more information on the brain scanning method used here (PET) and how the results are interpreted, see Box 2.2.

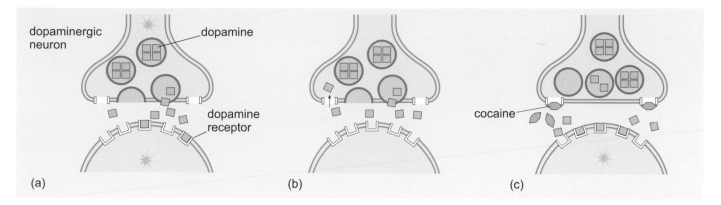

(a) (b) (c)

Figure 2.7 (a) Normal release of dopamine, in the absence of cocaine, from a dopaminergic neuron. (b) Following release, the neurotransmitter is promptly returned to the dopaminergic neuron via a reuptake channel or broken down by enzymes (not shown here). (c) In the presence of cocaine, the reuptake channel is blocked by the drug so that dopamine cannot be removed from the synapse as effectively after an action potential has triggered its release. This longer period in the synaptic gap increases the probability of dopamine binding to receptors and therefore increases the stimulation of the postsynaptic neuron.

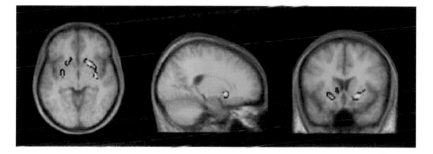

Figure 2.8 PET scans taken from three different views of the brain. These show decreased binding of radioactive substance at dopamine receptors in the presence of cocaine, as the drug increases the amount of dopamine in the synaptic gap and the neurotransmitter displaces the radioactive tracer from the receptors (see Book 1, Section 3.3.2).

Box 2.2 PET – positron emission tomography

It is possible to measure the electrical activity in the brain and, through this, to gain some insight into what regions of the brain are active in particular situations. However, the skull is a very good insulator of electrical activity and, as such, electrical signals become displaced and reduced in strength as they pass through the bone. An alternative to measuring the electrical activity of the brain is to measure blood flow within the brain.

The brain requires a continuous supply of blood to provide both energy, in the form of glucose, and oxygen. It can neither store these substances nor use alternatives. About 20% of the heart's output of blood goes to the brain.

However, the progress of the blood through the brain is not a flood, but a carefully controlled irrigation. The network of blood vessels in the brain is under very sensitive, localised control, such that each region of the brain receives only the amount of blood that it requires: all regions of the brain do not receive equal amounts. Those regions that receive the most blood during a particular activity (e.g. listening to a sound or performing a manual manipulation), and hence are in receipt of the most glucose and oxygen, are deemed to be the most active.

One device for measuring blood flow and distribution within the brain is an imaging technique called positron emission tomography (PET) (Book 1, Section 2.2.2). In a PET scan the patient or experimental participant has a small dose of radioactive material injected into their bloodstream, which is transported around the body and into the brain. This radioactive material emits small, high-energy particles called positrons. Each emitted positron interacts with a nearby electron, resulting in the annihilation of them both and the production of gamma-rays (a form of electromagnetic radiation like X-rays, but of higher energy). The gamma-rays disperse in equal and opposite directions from the point of positron–electron annihilation and can be detected by suitable sensors. A computer can reconstruct the source of the gamma-rays using information about which sensors are activated and when. The process of reconstruction is called tomography – the 'T' in PET. The regions of the brain that command the greater volumes of blood produce the most gamma-rays and it is these regions that are computed and displayed by the PET scan, an example of which is shown in Figure 2.9.

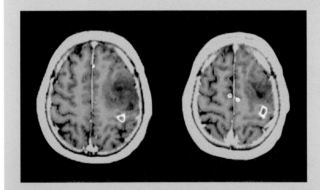

Figure 2.9 Example of two PET scan images taken at different horizontal levels whilst a participant finger tapped with the left hand. The front of the brain is towards the top of the figure. Activity is apparent in the right hemisphere. Colour has been added to show regions of high activation.

In some cases PET can use a radioactive substance that specifically binds to certain receptors in the brain. This method is sometimes used in studies of drugs like cocaine (see Book 1, Section 3.3.2): the radioactive substance is designed to bind to dopamine receptors but not as strongly as dopamine itself. When a drug like cocaine is given, the increase in natural dopamine levels at the synapse causes the radioactive substance to be displaced from the receptors, appearing as a decrease in activation on the PET image, as you have seen in Figure 2.8.

Whilst cocaine acts directly at the dopaminergic synapse to block dopamine reuptake channels, nicotine and heroin act indirectly to alter dopamine levels. Nicotine, for example, can bind to *nicotinic* receptors on the dopaminergic neuron which ordinarily would bind the natural neurotransmitter, acetylcholine (Book 1, Section 3.5.2). When the nicotine binds in the place of acetylcholine it increases the firing of action potentials in the dopaminergic neuron, which in turn will increase the release of dopamine. This is shown in Figure 2.10.

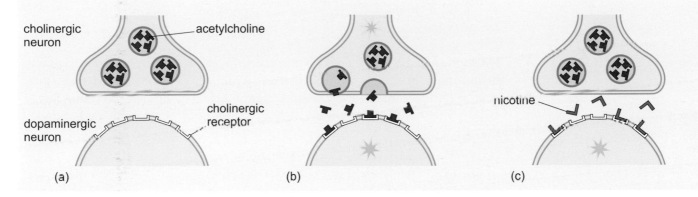

Figure 2.10 (a) and (b) In the absence of nicotine, the dopaminergic neuron can be activated by the binding of acetylcholine (released from a cholinergic neuron) to receptors on the dopaminergic neuron. (c) However, in the presence of nicotine, the dopaminergic neuron can be activated by nicotine, without the need for release of acetylcholine. This results in increased firing of the dopaminergic neuron and therefore increased release of dopamine.

Nicotine, specifically in the form of cigarettes, has also been shown to have additional effects on synaptic dopamine levels. This is because another substance in the tobacco smoke decreases the amount of a particular enzyme in the brain.

■ From your knowledge of the synapse, where might this enzyme normally act and how will decreasing the amount of the enzyme cause an increase in dopamine levels?

☐ The enzyme is likely to be the one that normally breaks down dopamine at the synapse; by decreasing the levels of this enzyme, the breakdown of dopamine becomes less efficient and the neurotransmitter will remain at the synapse for longer.

You have now seen how an addictive drug can increase dopamine levels by acting directly on the dopaminergic neuron to block reuptake (cocaine), or by exciting the dopaminergic neuron (nicotine) so that it releases dopamine. For the final example, we shall consider how heroin acts to increase dopamine levels. Heroin is chemically similar to a group of substances naturally found in our bodies called opioids and because of this structural similarity it is possible for heroin to bind to the receptors in the body that are normally occupied by these endogenous opioids (see Book 1, Section 2.4.2). Heroin is one of a number of drugs that can bind to these receptors (another is codeine); all of these drugs are referred to as opiates. In this instance, the receptors in question are located on GABAergic neurons, meaning that the neuron releases the neurotransmitter GABA. GABA is an inhibitory neurotransmitter, which means that it normally acts to prevent action potentials being produced in the postsynaptic neuron.

■   What would normally be the effect of the GABAergic neuron on the postsynaptic dopaminergic neuron activity and the levels of dopamine released?

☐   As GABA is an inhibitory neurotransmitter, activity in a GABAergic neuron would normally result in suppression or inhibition of the dopaminergic neuron, resulting in less dopamine being released.

Given that all addictive drugs increase the levels of dopamine at the synapse, heroin must, in some way, decrease this inhibitory action of the GABAergic neuron on the dopaminergic neuron. Heroin achieves this by inhibiting the GABAergic neuron when it binds to the opioid receptor. Figure 2.11 shows the effect this may have on the dopaminergic neuron.

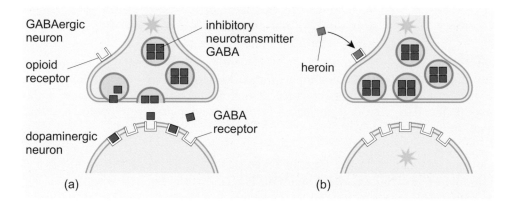

Figure 2.11   (a) Under normal heroin-free conditions dopaminergic neurons are inhibited by the neurotransmitter GABA. This reduces the frequency of action potentials in the dopaminergic neuron and therefore its release of dopamine. (b) When heroin binds to the opioid receptors on the GABAergic neuron it prevents the release of GABA. As the GABA is no longer released, it is no longer able to inhibit the dopaminergic neuron and therefore the dopaminergic neuron is able to fire and release dopamine in response to excitatory inputs. These excitatory inputs are not shown in part (b) but are assumed to be active, hence the dopaminergic neuron is shown to be firing and therefore releasing dopamine.

■   Do the actions of heroin give any insight into why the drug might be liked and associated with euphoria? Can the same be said of cocaine?

☐   Heroin acts on opioid receptors and it is likely that this action underlies a liking for the drug as taste reactivity tests show opioids mediate liking. The same cannot be said for cocaine as there is no mention of it acting on opioid receptors, only at dopaminergic synapses, which mediates the wanting rather than liking element of motivation.

Activity 2.1 Drugs and the brain
(LO 2.2) Allow 30 minutes

Now would be an ideal time to study the activity entitled 'Drugs and the brain', which you will find in the multimedia map. In this activity, you will be able to see the firing or activity of a dopaminergic neuron and the release of dopamine in the absence of various drugs. You will then be able to discover the effects of these drugs on the dopamine level at the synapse.

It should be noted that it is not only the action of these drugs on overall dopamine levels that is thought to be important; the rate at which the drug enters the brain is also critical in determining the effect it has. Faster entry is associated with a more intense 'high' and a stronger ability to promote repeated use and hence the possibility of becoming addicted (Volkow et al., 1995). Different methods of administration enable the drug to enter the brain more quickly. A study by Swanson and Volkow (2003) evaluated levels of methylphenidate, a drug similar to amphetamine, which you met in Activity 2.1, and cocaine, in the brain following oral and intravenous administration and the results are shown in Figure 2.12. To help you interpret the graph it might be useful to revisit Box 4.5 in Book 1.

■ Using Figure 2.12, estimate the amount of time taken to reach peak levels (100%) in the brain for the two types of administration. What does this suggest about which route of administration is likely to give the most intense 'high' to the user?

□ For intravenous administration the peak is reached after around 13 minutes whilst for orally administered methylphenidate the peak is reached approximately 85 minutes after administration. Given that the intensity of the high experienced is proportional to the rate at which the drug enters the brain, it is likely that the intravenous administration will give a more intense experience, which has indeed been found to be the case.

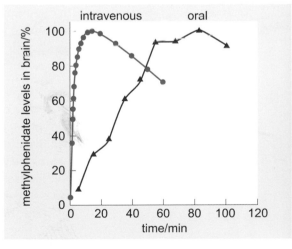
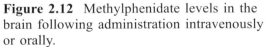

Figure 2.12 Methylphenidate levels in the brain following administration intravenously or orally.

When considering ways in which neurotransmission might be altered at the synapse, it is reasonably easy to see how drugs can do this, because they can actually move into the synapse and alter activity of the neurons. However, it is not only intake of drugs such as cocaine that can alter neurotransmission in this way; certain behaviours, such as gambling and sex, may elicit similar effects, which may explain why such behaviours can be considered to be addictive, as discussed in Chapter 1.

2.3.3 Dopamine and addictive behaviours

Addictive behaviours such as gambling have been shown to affect dopaminergic neurons, although the exact mechanism is unclear. For example, a study by Bergh et al. (1997) found that there were alterations to dopamine levels in the cerebrospinal fluid (CSF) (Book 2, Section 2.3.1). This fluid circulates slowly around the central nervous system and therefore can give an indication of the activity of the nervous system. CSF can be withdrawn in procedures such as a lumbar puncture in which the fluid is removed from the spinal cord using a hollow needle and syringe. This procedure can be carried out in humans as well as other animals.

■ Can you see any limitations in examining chemicals in the CSF?

☐ The CSF contains a variety of chemicals from throughout the CNS and therefore it is not possible to tell where the particular chemicals originated. It is also not easily limited to a particular point in time as it circulates slowly. This means that it would be difficult to link it to a specific event in the CNS.

In addition to the problems of tying the chemicals in CSF to a particular brain region or time point, having a lumbar puncture is an invasive procedure which is uncomfortable and also carries the risk of nerve damage; therefore there are ethical issues that need to be fully considered and appropriate permissions sought before such a study could be conducted.

Despite these limitations, studies examining the different chemicals in CSF can be useful. Bergh et al. (1997) found that the amount of dopamine in the CSF of gamblers in comparison to non-gamblers was much lower. However, the amount of dopamine metabolites (the products of the breakdown of dopamine by enzymes) was much higher. The authors suggested that these results are indicative of the amount of dopamine being released, and therefore broken down, being increased in the brains of gamblers.

More recently, imaging techniques have been used to investigate the effects of gambling on the brain. One particular study by Reuter et al. (2005) examined activation in the brain during a card game gambling task. They found that in healthy non-addicted individuals a number of brain regions, including the ventral striatum (which contains the nucleus accumbens), responded in a similar fashion to gambling-related stimuli as they might to cocaine, when measured using a scanning technique called fMRI (see Book 2, Box 4.3 for more information on this technique).

■ What is the significance of both gambling and cocaine activating the ventral striatum?

☐ The striatum includes the nucleus accumbens and this forms part of the mesolimbocortical pathway, which is involved in motivation (Section 2.2). Stimuli that can activate this pathway are likely to be capable of reinforcing the behaviour that leads to their activation.

Gambling is just one type of behaviour that individuals can become addicted to; also mentioned were people who become addicted to work, so-called workaholics. As yet there is very little evidence that the act of work can command control of the mesolimbocortical dopamine pathway, but research with monkeys has suggested that altering dopamine neurotransmission can make the monkeys work harder and more effectively. Research funded by the US government, and conducted by Dr Barry Richmond (Liu et al., 2004) at the National Institute of Mental Health, has shown that if the number of dopamine receptors, and therefore the amount of available binding sites for dopamine, in a region of the brain called the rhinal cortex is reduced, monkeys will work harder and produce fewer errors on a task – in this case, pressing a lever in exchange for drops of water. The researchers suggest that if the number of dopamine receptors decreases, the monkeys become less able to judge how much work they have done towards a goal and therefore maintain high levels of performance over long periods.

Of course, this is not the clear-cut evidence that is seen and accepted with other behaviours or drugs, as it merely demonstrates that altering dopamine neurotransmission using experimental techniques can alter work behaviour. However, despite a lack of firm evidence, it is becoming gradually accepted that work may have similar neurobiological actions to other addictive behaviours and drugs. Indeed, one of the models of addiction recovery, the 12-step programme (which will be discussed in Chapter 4), is used by the support group Workaholics Anonymous in much the same way that it is used by Alcoholics or Gamblers Anonymous.

You may recall from Section 1.3.3 that addictions can often occur in combination: for example, with an individual being addicted to both sex and cocaine. Hopefully, you now recognise that both of these can act to excite the dopaminergic neurons in the brain. One possible explanation for such activities being combined is that once the dopaminergic neurons are activated by one such stimulus, the effect carries to other stimuli, effectively increasing their motivational pull, resulting in individuals combining addictive activities.

2.4 Why might increased dopamine lead to addiction?

In this chapter, you have learnt that motivation can be divided into wanting and liking and that dopamine mediates the wanting element through its actions in the incentive motivation or mesolimbocortical pathway. You have also seen how addictive drugs and behaviour might increase dopamine levels at the synapses of this pathway.

■ How might this increased dopamine cause repetition of the behaviour or drug use?

□ Increased levels of dopamine release can act to increase the motivational pull or wanting for the behaviour or drug, effectively making them seem more attractive.

As the different drugs or behaviours increase levels of dopamine they increase their own *pull* over behaviour, essentially increasing their incentive value and therefore their ability to reinforce the behaviour that led to them, which might explain why a behaviour is repeated after first use or engagement.

However, addiction does not develop overnight and in some individuals it might never develop despite repeated use of drugs or engagement in addictive behaviours; so addiction is likely to be more complicated than the simple hijacking of one pathway within the brain to encourage repetition of behaviour. Therefore, whilst this pathway might provide the biological underpinnings of the acute and addictive effects of various drugs and behaviours, it is unlikely to be the full story.

2.5 Final word

Evidence suggests that there is a common neurobiological response to all addictive drugs and behaviours which involves the mesolimbocortical pathway. It is thought that all of these drugs and behaviours briefly increase the amount of dopamine at the synapse. Throughout this chapter we have focused on the immediate effects of these addictive drugs or behaviours on dopamine levels in the brain and how these immediate effects might lead to them being repeated. In Chapter 3 you will learn more about how addiction might arise in certain situations, by evaluating some of the main models of addiction. To do this we will widen our view back out from the biological to consider the other factors affecting addiction.

2.6 Summary of Chapter 2

- Addiction can be understood in the context of motivation and in particular, the mesolimbocortical dopamine pathway.
- There is evidence to suggest that there is a common neurobiological response to all addictive drugs and behaviours, which involves an increase in the amount of synaptic dopamine in this pathway in a manner also seen with natural incentives such as sex and food.
- The exact mechanism by which this happens varies: for example, the actions of opiates such as heroin are mediated through an inhibitory neuron but the overall outcome is the same.
- This increase in dopamine in the mesolimbocortical pathway is likely to have the effect of increasing the incentive value of the stimulus that caused it, which may explain why behaviour is repeated.

2.7 Learning outcomes

LO 2.1 Name the brain regions and neurotransmitters involved in motivation. (KU1)

LO 2.2 Explain, using experimental evidence, how addictive drugs may directly and indirectly alter dopamine levels. (KU1, KU2, KU5, CS1, CS2, CS5)

LO 2.3 Describe the evidence for behaviours such as gambling altering the dopaminergic functioning in the brain. (KU2, KU5, CS3)

2.8 Self-assessment questions

SAQ 2.1 (LO 2.1)

Which three regions of the brain are critical in motivation? Explain in which of these regions you would find the dopamine cell bodies and site of termination of the axons.

SAQ 2.2 (LO 2.2)

The effects of cocaine may be blocked by preventing the actions of dopamine at the synapse: for example, using a dopamine antagonist. One of the actions of heroin could also be blocked in this way, but can you think of any other ways it can be blocked?

SAQ 2.3 (LO 2.2)

How do the actions of cocaine differ from that of amphetamine? (*Hint*: you will need to complete Activity 2.1 to answer this question.)

SAQ 2.4 (LO 2.3)

The study by Reuter et al. (2005) mentioned in Section 2.3.3 used fMRI to investigate the effects of gambling on the brain. Does the study show that dopamine release increased in the brain following exposure to gambling-related stimuli for healthy individuals?

Chapter 3 Modelling addiction

Eleanor Dommett

3.1 Using models to understand addiction

In Chapter 1 you read that there are a number of factors – psychological, sociological and biological – which interact to determine whether an individual might initiate addictive behaviour or use of addictive drugs. In Chapter 2 you learnt more about the *acute* effects of these addictive behaviours and drugs on motivation; in particular, that they all share an ability to increase dopamine levels at the synapse. However, addiction is a chronic experience, defined by a long-term lack of control, in which the risk of relapse can continue even after long periods of abstinence. Given this chronic nature, it is, therefore, unlikely that the factors contributing to initiation of drug use or addictive behaviour (Chapter 1) and the short-term increases in synaptic dopamine levels (Chapter 2) can fully explain addiction. In this chapter we will examine some of the different models of addiction proposed by researchers, beginning with the biological models which follow on from Chapter 2 and progressing towards a broader, more integrated model.

The purpose of models in psychology can be considered to be twofold. Firstly, they can be used to further understand the behaviour being observed and therefore help us to understand the nature of it: for example, whether or not it should be classified as a mental health condition. Secondly, they can be used to help guide development of interventions and treatments. These two aims are not mutually exclusive and many models will aim to do and achieve both. However, in this chapter we will focus on how the models explain the behaviour observed in addiction, with less emphasis on what they tell us about treating addiction. In Chapter 4, we will focus on treatments and also consider how they relate, if at all, to the models discussed here.

Each of the models we will discuss has a slightly different emphasis, but all allow for addiction to develop through an escalation of use of the addictive drug or behaviour, such that it reaches a compulsive level that may be detrimental to the individual and those around them, resulting in the loss of control over the behaviour that is the hallmark of addiction.

- Can you think of examples where heroin use or gambling becomes detrimental to the individual and those around them?

- There are many different answers that you might have come up with, but here are some examples. Heroin use may become detrimental when the person is unable to function normally, with their life becoming chaotic. They may become unable to work, which will affect those around the drug user, for example, as other employees have to cover work commitments for them. Recall from Activity 1.1 that Gary talks of missed opportunities and relationships breaking down. Heroin use may also result in related health problems such as contraction of hepatitis C or HIV. In some cases a heroin user may turn to crime to fund their addiction. Gambling may become detrimental when the gambler becomes unable to support him or herself financially because they are spending their money gambling, or as Patrick reports in Activity 1.1, taking money to fund his gambling. At this point it is possible that friends or family may have to step in with financial support rather than see the gambler be made homeless or go hungry.

Before we examine the different models, it is useful to spend a little time asking exactly *what* we want a model of addiction to do.

When developing a model of a particular behaviour or illness, there are often key criteria the model should meet, irrespective of the specific behaviour or illness being modelled. For example, a model should be coherent and comprehensive and explain the observations made about the behaviour being modelled, such as how particular symptoms arise over a particular time course. A model of addiction, therefore, should explain how behaviour or drug use can escalate to levels of compulsion. It must also be able to explain why some people will use a drug or engage in a potentially addictive behaviour and never become addicted, whereas others become addicted after differing periods of experimental or controlled use/behaviour.

In order to be truly informative, a model of addiction should also indicate how it might be treated. These predictions of treatments, as with all scientific predictions, should be testable and falsifiable, meaning that they could, in theory be shown to be false through observation and testing.

We will now examine some different models of addiction and as we do so, you should keep the following four criteria in mind:

1   The model is capable of explaining how drug use or behaviour becomes, and can remain, compulsive; that is, the *development* and *maintenance* of addiction.

2   The model can explain the observed *features* of addiction. Specifically this might include some of the factors listed in DSM-IV-TR (Section 1.1.3): tolerance, withdrawal and craving.

3   The model can explain why only certain individuals develop addictions at certain times; that is, *individual differences* in addiction.

4   The model provides *treatment predictions* for addiction.

Activity 3.1 Evaluating models of addiction

(LOs 3.1 and 3.2) Allow 2 hours to complete this activity whilst working through the chapter

Now would be an ideal time to begin this activity by downloading the 'Evaluating models of addiction' table from the study planner for this week's study or drawing out your own version so that you can add to it as you work through this chapter. You will use this table to keep a record of how well the different models perform against the criteria listed above. As you work through this chapter you should only complete columns 1–5, as the 'Actual treatments' column will be completed during Chapter 4. (You might like to revisit Chapter 1 and the Glossary to remind yourself about these features of addiction.)

Model	Criterion 1 Development and maintenance	Criterion 2 Features: craving, tolerance and withdrawal	Criterion 3 Individual differences	Criterion 4 Treatment predictions	Actual treatments

3.2 Biomedical or 'disease' models of addiction

In Chapter 2 you learnt about the common neurobiology of addiction and in particular the role of dopamine in the acute effects of addictive drugs and behaviours. Given these common effects, it is perhaps unsurprising that there has been significant emphasis placed on biomedical models of addiction. For the most part, these models can be considered disease (or medical) models and their emphasis is on biological factors underlying development and maintenance of addiction.

When the disease model of addiction first materialised, it offered a significant advantage over models that saw addiction as a consequence of a character flaw. For example, if addiction is perceived as a disease rather than a choice, then the social stigma associated with it is reduced. Moreover, it was believed that by reducing blame, those with addictions would experience less guilt, which in turn would allow them to focus on recovery.

Despite these perceived benefits, there is also some fierce resistance to the idea of addiction being a disease. One of the most well-known arguments against addiction being a disease is described by Professor John Booth Davies in his book *The Myth of Addiction* (1997), in which he suggests that seeing addiction as a disease merely allows the addicted individual the convenience of playing the victim rather than being responsible for their own behaviour. He cites how addicted individuals talk about their addiction as evidence of this; in particular, he notes that when an individual with an addiction talks to health workers or police, he or she will use certain terms of addiction, talking of their loss of control and helplessness. By contrast, when talking to peers, these elements of the addiction are replaced with more rational thoughts and preferences, which is something we will return to in Section 3.3.1.

Booth Davies suggests that the disease concept also suits those working in professions that treat addiction and the families and friends of those with addictions, who find comfort in the idea of a loss of control, rather than unwise decisions. In addition to Booth Davies' controversial argument against addiction being a disease, others have objected to this model on the basis of what a disease really is. For example, some would consider a disease as being caused by a known pathology or pathogen which can be detected by laboratory tests. Heart disease, for instance, can be detected using tests examining blood flow through the heart or electrical impulses from the heart, but no such test exists for addiction. However, this argument could be used to suggest that all mental disorders, none of which can be detected with a simple laboratory test, are not diseases. The second reason often used for rejecting addiction as a disease is that the use of addictive drugs and the practice of addictive behaviours are continuous with controlled behaviours. This means that there is no clear place to draw a line between the behaviour of the addicted individual and that of the non-addicted. However, advocates of the disease model would suggest that this is also true in other diseases such as hypertension, where there is a continuum of blood pressure between healthy individuals and those who have the disease.

Assuming then that these criticisms can be adequately countered and that addiction *could* be considered a disease, what exactly does the model say about addiction? In fact, there are two different incarnations of the disease model of addiction. The first is the susceptibility model which essentially suggests that addicts are born, not made. The second is the exposure model which suggests that addiction arises as a consequence of changes in the brain that occur with repeated use of addictive drugs or behaviours. We shall now consider each of these models in turn, but before doing so it is important to acknowledge that the two are not mutually exclusive.

3.2.1 The susceptibility model of addiction

In order to evaluate the susceptibility model, which essentially states that controlled use of addictive drugs or engagement with additive behaviours is not possible, we will consider what evidence there is for a genetic influence on addiction. However, before we do this, it is important to acknowledge that proponents of this model recognise that although the genes involved play a critical role, they do so in the context of social and environmental factors.

Early family-based studies comparing the probability of substance use disorders in relatives have suggested that addictive disorders may have some element of heritability (Book 2, Box 2.2), or put another way, they can be attributed to genetic factors, rather than environmental ones. For example, a large study has shown that close relatives of addicted individuals were on average eight times more likely to have a problem with substance use than those related to non-addicted individuals, as shown in Figure 3.1.

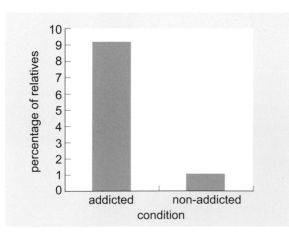

- Given the neurobiological evidence presented in Chapter 2 suggesting that all addictive behaviours and drugs have similar biological effects, would you expect relatives to be at risk from *any* addiction or the *same* addiction as their family member?

- The risk is likely to be for any addiction rather than the same addiction.

- The reason for investigating addiction in family members is that they are genetically very similar, but what else, other than genes, do family members share?

Figure 3.1 The percentage of relatives with a substance use problem is around eight times higher in those related to an addicted individual in comparison to those related to non-addicted individuals. Data adapted from Merikangas et al. (1998).

☐ Family members will often share an environment as well: for example, brothers and sisters will often be brought up together and even the environment shared in the womb (for twins, both identical and non-identical) may have an effect.

In order to get round this confounding factor of shared environments, adoption studies can be used, whereby correlations between the child, their biological parent and their adoptive parent are examined.

■ If the characteristic being examined were found to be strongly correlated between the child and their biological parent but not their adoptive parent, would this suggest a genetic or environmental basis?

☐ As the correlation is between the child and their biological parent, it is likely to have a genetic basis, because the child does not share their environment with their biological parent; rather they share this with their adoptive parent.

Indeed, substance abuse research has suggested that there is a strong correlation between the child and their biological parent, supporting a genetic influence in developing substance use disorders.

In addition to family and adoption studies, twin studies are often used, whereby correlations between identical twins are compared with correlations between non-identical twins. These studies have suggested that around 30% of the variation (Book 2, Box 2.1 on heritability) seen in stimulant (e.g. cocaine) abuse and addiction and 55% of the variation seen in heroin abuse and addiction (Tsuang et al., 2001) can be attributed to genetic factors.

The majority of the studies conducted relate to late stages in drug use (i.e. abuse and addiction), but it is possible that a genetic influence is actually affecting earlier, experimental use. For example, there may be genetic factors that predispose an individual to drug exposure and experimentation, such as the genes encoding dopamine receptors, which are associated with novelty-seeking behaviour. Should the receptor levels, which are coded for by the individual's genes, result in them displaying novelty-seeking behaviours, it is quite possible they will have an increased probability of experimentation with addictive drugs or behaviours and therefore an increased probability of becoming addicted. In addition, remember that these genetic factors will interact with social factors, for example affecting the choice of friends or peers.

Therefore, genetic influences may shape a number of behaviours that increase or decrease an individual's risk of becoming addicted. It is important to point out here that there is no single gene that predisposes to addiction; rather there are multiple genes which may make small contributions to relevant behaviours.

Evaluating the susceptibility model

Now would be a good time to evaluate this model according to our criteria and complete the row in your table in Activity 3.1. As this is the first model to be evaluated, you might find it helpful to read the next section first where we discuss the different criteria which should guide you through your evaluation.

Firstly, can this model account for the development and maintenance of addiction? The answer to this question is yes. Although the model does not attempt to explain why or how the behaviour comes to escalate to levels of compulsion, it assumes that in certain individuals controlled use is simply not possible and therefore when such an individual engages with the addictive drug or behaviour, they become addicted and this addiction is maintained.

Secondly, can the model account for defining features of addiction such as craving, tolerance and withdrawal? The model makes no attempt to directly explain these features but one could assume they might arise through multiple genes including those that code for dopamine receptors.

Thirdly, does the model explain individual differences in the development of addiction? Yes, this model does make predictions as to why some people become addicted and others do not, by basically suggesting that the genetic make-up of individuals influences their behaviours, with certain behaviours such as novelty-seeking being more likely to result in addiction.

Finally, does the model make any predictions about how addiction might be treated? This model predicts that controlled use is not possible and therefore any treatment must aim for complete abstinence. The model could also identify populations who should be targeted for preventive intervention strategies (Section 4.2) through their genetic make-up.

3.2.2 Exposure model of addiction

This model essentially states that changes in the brain arise through repeated exposure to an addictive drug or behaviour and that these changes underlie the switch to compulsive behaviour and therefore the development of addiction. Furthermore, once these changes have occurred they will effectively alter behaviour in a way that maintains the addiction.

This idea of addiction resulting from specific changes in the brain has meant that scientists have spent the last 30 years looking for these changes and producing detailed models of how they might result in addiction. Given the plethora of data, we shall consider only the two most influential exposure models before returning to our criteria and an evaluation of whether addiction can be considered the result of changes in the brain. As you read about these two models, you should consider them separately in your table, even though they can both come under the umbrella of the exposure model.

Incentive sensitisation

The most prominent model to arise from the field of neurobiology is that of **incentive sensitisation** which was first put forward by Robinson and Berridge in 1993. They suggested that addiction develops because the object of the addiction, such as heroin or work, becomes increasingly *wanted* over time. They suggest that the addictive drug or behaviour simply becomes so wanted that it commands attention beyond normal levels, such that the individual is compelled to use the drug or perform the behaviour in question. In order for this model to be plausible, there would need to be evidence that the brain regions and neurotransmitter involved in incentive motivation (Section 2.2) did indeed show enhanced reactivity or **sensitisation** over time.

■ Can you remember which pathway and structures are involved in incentive motivation?

☐ The mesolimbocortical pathway is involved in incentive motivation. This consists of dopaminergic neurons in the ventral tegmental area that extend their axons to both a region of the ventral striatum called the nucleus accumbens and the prefrontal cortex.

In Chapters 1 and 2 you learnt that the Skinner box can be used to determine how much *work* an animal will do in order to receive a reinforcer such as a drug. This paradigm has been particularly useful in looking for evidence for incentive sensitisation in addiction. This is because if sensitisation has occurred, it might be expected that the animal will work harder to receive a drug following initial exposure. Indeed, rats have been shown to work faster and harder for drugs such as amphetamine, cocaine and heroin following prior exposure to the drug, suggesting that sensitisation has occurred.

Similar results have been found with human participants. One particular study, using healthy adult volunteers, was carried out by Boileau et al. (2006). This study involved administering amphetamine, three times over a 5-day period and measuring dopamine levels in the nucleus accumbens. Measurements were taken using PET scanning (Figure 3.2; Box 2.2) to collect images before and after the amphetamine was given, so that researchers could calculate the differences between the two scans. Dopamine levels were assessed in response to amphetamine after the first dose was received on day 1 as well as in response to further doses administered 21 days and 365 days later.

■ From your knowledge of the actions of amphetamine from Activity 2.1, do you think dopamine levels in the nucleus accumbens would have increased or decreased in response to amphetamine?

☐ The dopamine levels are likely to increase because reuptake would be blocked and additional dopamine release may be triggered by the amphetamine.

■ If this study is to support the incentive sensitisation model of addiction, how do you think the levels of dopamine recorded on day 1 compare to those recorded 365 days later?

☐ The incentive sensitisation model suggests that the mesolimbocortical pathway involved in incentive motivation should become more sensitive to amphetamine. Therefore if the study supports this model, the levels of dopamine 365 days later should be higher than the levels on day 1.

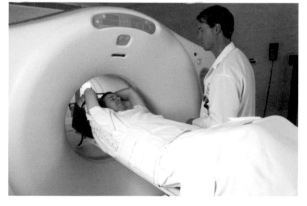

Figure 3.2 A participant entering a PET scanner.

Indeed, researchers found dopamine levels were increased in response to amphetamine on day 1, but that the levels were increased further on the 21- and 365-day tests. What does this study tell us about sensitisation? Well, it shows that the mesolimbocortical pathway responded more strongly to the drug following prior exposure even when that exposure was a year previously. This suggests two important points: firstly, that the mesolimbocortical pathway was more sensitive (it had been sensitised) to amphetamine; and secondly, that this sensitisation is long-lasting.

■   Can you remember why it is important to identify a long-lasting biological effect when trying to explain addiction?

☐   Addiction is a chronic condition which means that to explain it, we must find an effect which is equally long-lasting.

What is perhaps most interesting is that the level of sensitisation produced, as indicated by the amount of dopamine, was related to how impulsive and novelty-seeking the individual's rated themselves as being, with more impulsive, novelty-seeking individuals showing greater sensitisation. This offers some manner in which the sensitisation of individuals may differ and therefore why the development of addictions differs among people.

To summarise the story so far then, although actual dopamine release is transient because the dopamine is removed from the synapse, the dopaminergic neurons of the mesolimbocortical pathway show increased sensitivity or reactivity over longer periods. These findings therefore suggest, as the exposure model proposes, that long-term changes in the brain do occur following repeated drug use.

You may remember from Section 1.1.4 that individuals addicted to gambling may feel most driven to gamble when they are exposed to sights that reminded them of gambling. For example, seeing a fruit machine in a pub might evoke a strong urge to gamble even after long periods of abstinence. This craving, triggered by stimuli associated with the target of the addiction, is common to all addictions.

■   Can you think of another example of a stimulus related to the addiction which may trigger addictive behaviour?

☐   A commonly reported example is that being in a pub (or beer garden since the change in smoking legislation) can trigger a desire to smoke as drinking and smoking often co-occur in social settings. You might also recall Vic in Activity 1.1 mentioning that his desire to smoke is strong after a meal.

In order to understand how the sight or sound of a fruit machine can evoke such strong urges we have to return to classical conditioning. Recall that classical conditioning is the pairing of a neutral stimulus with an unconditional stimulus such that the formerly neutral stimulus becomes capable of producing a response that is normally reserved for the unconditional stimulus.

■   Can you identify the neutral and unconditional stimuli in the smoking example given above?

□   The pub or meal is the neutral stimulus and the nicotine in the cigarette is the unconditional stimulus.

Supporters of the incentive sensitisation model suggest that as neutral stimuli become associated with unconditional stimuli (the object of addiction) they acquire **incentive salience**, a kind of conditioned motivation that results in the ability to drive behaviour in a similar way to the original unconditioned stimulus. Importantly, there is some strong evidence for a conditioned motivational response occurring within the brain. In Chapter 2, you saw that all addictive drugs could elicit a response from dopaminergic neurons. This response is illustrated in Figure 3.3a, where the rewarding stimulus given could be a drug such as cocaine. The key thing to note is that after repeated pairings with a conditional stimulus (CS) such as a visual or auditory cue, the peak in dopaminergic neuron activity shifts forward in time to the CS rather than the reward (Figure 3.3b). This means that after conditioning, whenever such a conditional stimulus occurs, it can trigger a similar motivational response as the original reward.

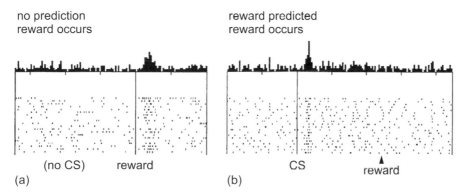

Figure 3.3 Data demonstrating how a dopaminergic neuron responds to rewarding or reinforcing stimuli and conditional stimuli. (a) Initially the dopaminergic neuron increases activity (firing and therefore release of dopamine) following the reward. (b) After repeated pairing of the reward with a conditional stimulus (CS), the dopaminergic neuron begins to increase activity in response to only the CS and not the reward. On each graph, there is a histogram showing activity directly above a raster plot (dots) in which each row represents a trial and each dot represents an action potential. Across a number of trials, the dopaminergic neuron consistently increased or decreased its firing at the same points. Data from Schultz et al. (1998).

Interestingly, the incentive salience of these associated, previously neutral stimuli can be affected by stress, which as you may recall is important in both the early, controlled engagement with addictive behaviours and drugs as well as in addiction and relapse. Scientists have found that the presence of corticotropin-releasing factor (CRF, a key chemical in the stress response, Book 2, Section 2.2.6) can amplify incentive salience (Pecina et al., 2006). The effect of this is to make the pull of the addictive drug or behaviour on motivation even stronger in a stressful situation. In addition, long-term stress is thought to sensitise the dopaminergic pathways, such that even after the stress has ceased, the pathways remain highly responsive to addictive drugs and behaviours (Goodman, 2008).

So far, you have learnt that the dopamine response to a drug can sensitise with time and that this sensitisation might drive compulsive behaviour. You have also seen that a gradual increase, or sensitisation, of the dopamine response to a previously neutral stimulus associated with a reinforcer could explain craving in some situations and that stress can impact on sensitisation, but is there any evidence to contradict this theory of addiction?

Perhaps unsurprisingly there is some evidence that the mesolimbocortical pathway does *not* sensitise during addiction. For example, individuals addicted to cocaine appear to show a decrease in dopamine release in response to methylphenidate (a drug similar to amphetamine and cocaine) in comparison to non-addicted controls, which is the direct opposite of what the incentive sensitisation model would predict (Volkow et al., 1997). However, the founders of this model, Robinson and Berridge (2008), argue that these data are not entirely reliable, because sensitisation is context-dependent. Although this might sound like a 'get-out clause', it is worthy of some consideration. Can you think of a moment when you have really wanted something, but when the same thing is available in a different context you no longer desire it? For many people, certain social environments might, for example, make them want to dance. However, if asked if they want to dance on a Tuesday at 11 a.m. whilst they sat at their desk or in a meeting, they would perhaps show very little desire to do so (Figure 3.4). It can of course be argued that the addicted individual would want to engage with the object of their addiction at all times; and that this is *exactly* what makes them addicted. But we have already heard that craving can be much stronger in certain contexts and that the experience of addiction can be limited to the experience of certain environments (such as the example of the Vietnam War veterans, in Section 1.3.1).

(a)   (b)

Figure 3.4 Context can make a difference to motivations to perform particular behaviours.

The incentive sensitisation model of addiction therefore proposes that with repeated engagement, the drug or behaviour and associated stimuli become increasingly wanted due to sensitisation of the mesolimbocortical pathway. According to this model, the increased wanting increases the ability of the drug or addictive behaviour to drive behaviour such that it can result in compulsion. This sensitisation seems to be context-dependent, to correlate with certain personality traits, and to be affected by stress and persist over long periods of abstinence.

Evaluating incentive sensitisation

So how does this model stand up to our four criteria for evaluating models of addiction? Before you continue reading, consider for yourself how this model meets the four criteria, completing the table from Activity 3.1 for the incentive sensitisation model.

Firstly, does the model explain how addiction can develop and be maintained? Yes, the model provides a robust neurobiological mechanism for a way in which repeated engagement with addictive drugs or behaviour can cause compulsion through the incentive motivation pathway becoming sensitised. It also explains the persistence of addiction because the changes that occur in the brain can last long into abstinence.

Secondly, does the model explain some of the observed features of addiction such as craving, tolerance and withdrawal? The incentive sensitisation model does indeed do this, with strong experimental evidence demonstrating why craving might occur more in particular settings: for example, in the presence of cues previously associated with the object of addiction. However, the model posits that the opposite of tolerance should occur because it predicts greater sensitivity rather than poorer and does not make reference to withdrawal.

Thirdly, can the model account for individual differences in the development of addiction? Yes, this model does offer an attractive explanation as to why certain individuals will become addicted, by suggesting that particular personality traits such as novelty-seeking, which may be affected by genes related to dopamine (Section 3.2.1), can make a person more likely to show sensitisation and therefore become addicted.

Finally, does the model offer any predictions for treating addiction? The implicit prediction from this model is that if addiction is caused by changes in the brain with repeated exposure, then a treatment that reverses these changes should be effective. In addition, the model recognises the importance of conditional responses and therefore predicts that reducing exposure to associated stimuli could reduce relapse. Also, the effect of stress is acknowledged and therefore any treatment that reduces stress would be in line with this model.

The incentive sensitisation model, therefore, stands up to the four criteria reasonably well. Perhaps unsurprisingly, it is a popular model with a large evidence base.

We shall now move on to consider a second exposure model of addiction.

Opponent motivational process

Although this model is being discussed second, it was actually proposed before the incentive sensitisation model in the 1970s by Solomon and Corbit

(1974); however, a more recent incarnation of the model will be the focus here. In addition, although it has been included here as a biomedical or disease model, there is significantly less consensus on which parts of the brain and which neurotransmitters are involved in the opponent motivational process model. The hallmark of this model is that it includes a much more prominent role for the negative effects of addictive drugs and behaviours than incentive sensitisation.

■ Can you think of any negative effects of the consumption of alcohol?

□ There are a variety of negative effects, depending on the timescale over which we look. For example, in the short term, alcohol can leave people bloated and sick with a hangover.

In order to understand the current version of this model, the original model by Solomon and Corbit (1974) will be briefly considered. They first suggested that the euphoria experienced immediately after drug intake or engaging in certain behaviours such as sex, is followed by an opposing response automatically made by the body; a kind of mood see-saw. This response is the **opponent motivational process**. This idea is not dissimilar to homeostasis, the mechanism by which our internal environment is kept constant. You might find it helpful to consider the basis of this model as a disruption to the homeostatic mechanism that deals with mood.

In the early stages of drug use or non-addicted gambling, for example, the positive mood evoked is soon balanced out by the automatic see-saw in the brain and, as shown in Figure 3.5a, everything returns to normal. It was hypothesised that in these early stages behaviour is driven by the desire to experience an immediate positive or euphoric mood (i.e. positive reinforcement). However, as behaviour such as drug-taking increases, Solomon and Corbit suggested that the positive effects become smaller and the negative effects become larger, as shown in Figure 3.5b. They suggested that, from this point onwards, the individual is compelled to continue the behaviour in order to relieve the terrible low moods experienced, meaning that they are now driven by negative reinforcement rather than positive reinforcement.

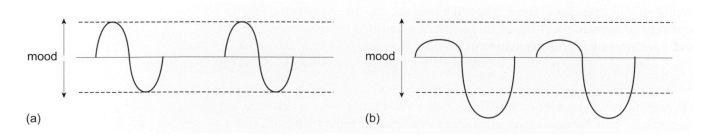

Figure 3.5 (a) The opponent motivational processes in the brain set up an automatic negative swing following a positive mood change. After the negative opponent process, mood returns to normal, baseline levels. (b) Solomon and Corbit suggested that over time the positive mood changes decrease in amplitude whilst the negative opponent motivational processes increase in size.

■ What is the term given to the negative effects experienced when an addicted individual is denied their drug?

□ Withdrawal.

Solomon and Corbit's original model fitted with the ideas of the time, of individuals addicted to drugs such as alcohol and heroin in desperate pain during withdrawal, but it was less effective in explaining addiction to drugs such as amphetamine, or behaviours, where the negativity is less pronounced. Moreover, there was some debate as to whether these negative effects, even if present, were capable of driving addiction. Given that the negative effects associated with withdrawal might only last one week, scientists started to doubt that these effects could explain the long-term nature of addiction.

This criticism was largely responsible for the opponent motivational process model going to ground for some time, but it did not disappear entirely – it has come to the forefront of addiction research, as a revamped version (Koob and Le Moal, 2008), 35 years after its first incarnation. In this newer version of the model, it is still maintained that during the early stages of drug use or engagement in addictive behaviours, the individual is driven by the positive reinforcing nature of the drug or behaviour. However, as the drug-taking or behaviour is repeated, they suggest a form of sensitisation occurs, in much in the same way as suggested by the incentive sensitisation model, resulting in increased wanting. This increased wanting results in an increased use of the drug or engagement in the behaviour, at which point the opponent processes start to dominate.

However, this is not because they get bigger as suggested in the original model, for which there was little evidence. Rather, the opponent processes *appear* to increase in size because the processes do not have time to reset between repetitions of drug use or behaviour.

To see how this might happen, consider the example of working your way towards completing an assignment. As the deadline draws near, you may experience some stress; however, if you submit it on time, you can relax and then move on to the next block of work, for which you will have adequate time. Conversely, if you do not submit the assignment on time and your tutor grants you an extension, you are not likely to have any time to relax before you start to prepare for the next one – you are continuously playing catch-up and your stress levels never return to normal.

The opponent motivational process model of addiction is a bit like your study planner: while everything runs smoothly and you finish each chapter on time, the balance of stress to relaxation is returned to normal. However, should the balance not be returned to normal from one event, it will overlap with the changes that occur in response to the next and the effects will summate. Figure 3.6 shows how this might happen with mood when taking a drug.

If the system is gradually spiralling downwards, the individual will find it harder and harder to experience the positive mood of first use. This might materialise as tolerance, the process whereby an addicted individual appears to need more and more of their desired drug or behaviour in order to feel good.

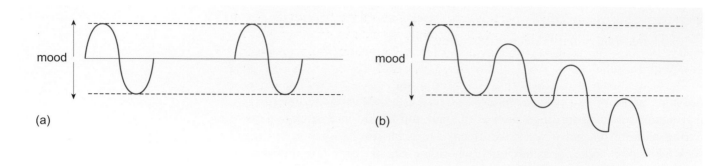

Figure 3.6 (a) Initially motivational processes have time to return to normal between cycles. (b) However, as the cycles become more frequent, there is no time to return to normal, which results in a gradual shift of the processes until they operate in a constant negative state, which can give the impression of increased opponent motivational processes.

The presence of tolerance therefore supports this model. But is there any evidence for where in the brain and how these opponent processes might occur? In fact, scientists have suggested that the mesolimbocortical pathway could mediate both the initial, positive effects and the negative opponent effects. For example, researchers have found that there is a decrease in dopamine release and receptor levels in addicted individuals, which could explain how tolerance arises.

- If there are fewer dopamine receptors, would you expect the effect of dopamine released at the synapse to be bigger or smaller?

☐ The effect would be smaller because there are fewer sites for dopamine to bind to before being removed from the synapse.

Moreover, these changes in dopamine receptors and release have been found to persist for years after abstinence, unlike acute withdrawal symptoms, meaning that they could explain the persistence of addiction.

You may recall that this evidence stands in direct contrast to the study by Boileau et al. (2006), discussed in support of incentive sensitisation, where they found increases in dopamine release over time. At present then, evidence is very mixed and it would be accurate to say that the jury is still out and more research will need to be done before any firm conclusions can be made.

As well as changes within the mesolimbocortical pathway, there are changes elsewhere in the brain, particularly in the stress system, which could also mediate opponent processes. For example, there are increased levels of CRF following chronic drug administration (Rivier et al., 1984) and blocking the actions of CRF appears to block the increased intake associated with addiction to cocaine, opioids, alcohol and nicotine (Koob and Le Moal, 2008). This role for stress essentially means that there are likely to be differences between individuals according to how well they cope with stress, which may depend on a variety of factors such as cognitive appraisal and temperament (Book 2, Section 2.2).

To summarise, this model of addiction suggests that drug use or behaviour is initially driven by the immediate positive effects, and that this could result in incentive sensitisation which increases the frequency of the behaviour. As this happens, the opponent processes which normally operate to reverse the acute positive effects of the drug or behaviour, start to dominate. These opponent processes are likely to be mediated by dopamine and the stress system. Once these opponent processes have taken hold, the brain regions and chemicals involved begin to operate outside the normal range and this is experienced as negativity, which drives further drug use or behaviour to restore the system to normal levels.

Evaluating opponent motivational process

We will now return to our criteria to evaluate this model but before we do, take a few minutes to do this yourself, completing the table from Activity 3.1 as you do so.

Firstly, does the model explain how addiction develops and is maintained? This model explains the development of compulsive behaviour in a similar way to the incentive sensitisation model, because it relics on sensitisation to increase behaviour. The model explains the maintenance of the behaviour through a desire to reduce the opponent processes or negative effects.

Secondly, does the model explain the observed features of addiction such as craving, tolerance and withdrawal? As with the first criterion, this model performs as well as the incentive sensitisation model in explaining craving. It also explains why tolerance and withdrawal may appear through the opponent processes.

Thirdly, does the model explain individual differences in addiction development? The model performs rather well on this criterion because it can explain individual differences as much as incentive sensitisation which it assumes may underlie the initial increase in frequency of the behaviour, but it also allows differences in the stress system, and therefore psychosocial and environmental factors such as stress and coping ability, to impact on addiction development.

Finally, does the model make any predictions about treatments? The opponent motivational process model makes the same predictions about treatment as the incentive sensitisation model, in that treatment should focus on reversing the sensitisation and reducing exposure to conditioned stimuli as well as reducing stress. Critically, anything that reduces the opponent processes should be beneficial according to this model. Unfortunately, the exact mechanisms of the opponent processes are still somewhat elusive beyond the likely candidate neurotransmitters and systems (i.e. dopamine and stress).

Although two different exposure models are presented above, it is important to remember that they are not mutually exclusive; that is to say, both may be important. They can be considered as members of a running team who all have a slightly different style; one might jog whilst another sprints. There are certain times in the run, when one person's style is perhaps more appropriate and the same is true of addiction models. For example, the incentive sensitisation model offers a good explanation of why craving is strongest in the presence of associated stimuli whilst the opponent motivational process model offers some useful insight into how tolerance might occur. Both also offer a mechanism through which stress may trigger relapse.

Before we move on, refer to your table for Activity 3.1: do you think the disease models of addiction stand up well to all the criteria? You will probably see that the susceptibility model only covers three of the four criteria, as it does not account for the features of addiction and, where it does contribute, the focus is on genetic influences rather than actual mechanisms for *how* addiction can arise and be maintained in some individuals and how it might be treated. In contrast, both types of exposure model fare better on all four criteria. However, you will notice that these models do focus at the level of the biology rather than that of psychological factors such as choice and attention (although personality traits are mentioned). Therefore we will now consider models that focus on psychological factors.

3.3 Psychological models of addiction

You have seen that whilst the biomedical or disease models of addiction can provide insights into how the brain changes in response to repeated exposure to addictive drugs or behaviours, they do not allow for all of the significant psychological factors influencing addiction. It is perhaps then not surprising that psychologists have also produced models of addiction, some of which stand in contrast to the biomedical or disease models and others which might complement them. In this section you will learn about two such models. As you work through both models, remember to complete your table for Activity 3.1 and also to consider how these models compare to those outlined above.

3.3.1 A rational choice model of addiction

When attempting to explain any behaviour, psychologists often find it convenient to start from the assumption that all behaviour arises from rational choice, where the individual considers whether the expected benefit of behaving in a particular way will outweigh the cost. The first model of addiction we shall consider then is that addiction can be explained through rational choice. For many people, the intuitive response to this is simply that addiction *cannot* arise in this way, but this argument is based on the observations of non-addicted individuals that no one would choose to live with an addiction. For example, non-addicted individuals find it hard to understand why an individual addicted to heroin would choose to live in a dirty squat or why a gambler would choose gambling over his or her family; but should the assumptions of other, non-addicted people be sufficient to conclude that there is no rational choice in addiction? Perhaps not, especially when the non-addicted observers often focus on the longer-term consequences of the addiction (e.g. the choice to live in a squat) rather than the shorter-term experience of taking heroin, whilst individuals with an addiction may focus on the latter in making their choice. Assuming then that the intuitions of non-addicted individuals are not sufficient to rule out a role for choice in addiction, can this model explain how addiction arises and is maintained?

To answer this question, we need to know what we mean by rational:

> Having the faculty of reasoning; endowed with reason.
>
> *(Concise Oxford English Dictionary, 2009)*

As you can see from the definition, to make a rational choice simply means to reason, that is to make a judgement – a cost–benefit analysis – for a particular behaviour. Therefore, although it is often assumed that addiction cannot arise through rational choice, if this simply means to consider, rather than 'make the right choice', then is it perhaps plausible that addiction might arise through rational choice? This is a controversial viewpoint and you would be hard pushed to find anyone who would agree that they chose to become addicted. It is one thing to choose to initiate a behaviour such as gambling or experimental use of a drug, but quite another to choose to become addicted to it. However, it is plausible that an individual might choose addiction if they feel the benefits of the behaviour outweigh the cost – perhaps life without their addiction would be even worse. For example, an individual may choose addiction, rather than accept their life without it, which may be empty and difficult. Bryan, in his addiction to work (Vignette 1.2), may well illustrate such an example. So perhaps rational choice could underlie the *development* of some addictions, but can it underlie the *maintenance* of addiction?

There is a strong indication that there is something more than rational choice involved in maintaining addiction. If it were simply a case of choice, then why can someone not give up their addiction as soon as they decide to do so? Recall from Activity 1.1 that Robin made a number of attempts to give up heroin but always returned to using the drug. This would suggest that Robin was not choosing to maintain his addiction – quite the opposite, he wanted to stop taking the drug. Should we then conclude that this rational choice model cannot explain how addiction is maintained?

Not necessarily – consider the following example, which might explain why efforts of restraint often fail despite rational choice. When was the last time you underestimated the amount of time it would take you to do something – for example, reading a chapter of SDK228 or completing an assignment? Many of us are not very good at predicting the consequences of a particular behaviour and therefore perhaps making informed choices, so why should an addicted individual be any better at this?

In the question above, you could equally have asked yourself when was the last time you changed your mind; for example, regarding what you were going to wear or whether to eat dinner in the kitchen or living room. In everyday life, our preferences are unstable – they change over time. We change our minds regularly and our behaviours change in line with this. Therefore, it is perhaps unfair to suggest that an individual with an addiction should be any different in their preferences towards that addiction than other individuals are in their preferences to other behaviours. If we now assume that choices can be rational (without necessarily being seen as right) and poorly informed and unstable, then can we explain addiction with choice?

Robert West (2006) suggests that if we can accept that the appearance and maintenance of addiction is simply the consequence of rational choices being made on a backdrop of uninformed cost–benefit analysis and unstable preferences, as may be the case for decisions by non-addicted individuals as well, then this rational choice model can be useful in understanding addiction.

Although it was pointed out earlier that you would be hard pushed to find an addicted individual who would agree that they chose their addiction, recall from Section 3.2 that John Booth Davies states that when an addicted individual is talking to peers (as opposed to health or legal professionals, for example), they express considerable rational thought and preference about their addiction, which is supportive of a role for rational choice. Before we consider a second psychological model, take a few minutes to evaluate this model according to our four criteria and add your conclusions to the table for Activity 3.1.

Evaluating the rational choice model

Firstly, does the model explain the development and maintenance of addiction? Yes; the model suggests that addiction can arise and be maintained as a result of rational, uninformed and unstable choice, although no exact mechanism is given.

Secondly, does this model explain the features of addiction such as craving, tolerance and withdrawal? The model does not mention any of the key features.

Thirdly, does the model explain the individual differences in addiction? There is little mention of this but one could assume that these individual differences arise simply through people making different, individual decisions.

Finally, does the model make any predictions about how addiction should be treated? If addiction is considered a rational choice, then presumably choice must also be at the centre of treatment – the individual must choose to stop behaving in a particular way or taking a particular drug. In line with this, providing individuals with additional information to make more informed decisions could be helpful in treating addiction according to this model.

- Can you think why putting choice at the centre of addiction treatment could be unhelpful?

☐ If others assume that the individual is choosing to maintain their addiction, or at the very least, not choosing to stop it, then they may be blamed for their addiction, which could be counterproductive in treatment.

To summarise then, whilst addiction could result from rational choice, this model is too limited to be considered a comprehensive model of addiction, accounting for none of the key diagnostic features. Furthermore, it has fallen out of favour, largely because it allows blame to be laid at the door of the individual with the addiction, which can be counterproductive.

3.3.2 Addiction as a cognitive bias

The cognitive bias model of addiction is perhaps the best known of the psychological models and it states that addiction arises out of, or is maintained by, a tendency of the addicted individual to pay greater attention to, and selectively remember, particular information about their addiction. Specifically, it is suggested that cognitive biases in beliefs about the costs and benefits of a particular behaviour cause biases in attention and memory towards drug- or addictive-behaviour-related stimuli which can drive the individual towards the object of their addiction.

One of the main methods used to investigate the presence of cognitive biases in addiction is a modified version of the Stroop task, which you first met in Book 1 (Section 3.5.1). Before an explanation of how the test is modified, we turn to a brief reminder about the normal Stroop task and what it measures. The Stroop task relies on the fact that most humans are so proficient at reading and processing words that they do so automatically, so much so that to ignore the words on the pages takes considerable cognitive effort. The task takes advantage of the fact that we are quicker at reading words than we are at naming the colour of the word, by colouring words in a way that is inconsistent with the actual word: for example, writing the word green in red ink. When one reads such a word, the tendency is to give the actual word (i.e. green) rather than the colour in which it is printed (in this case red), which is what is required in the Stroop task.

Activity 3.2 The Stroop task

(LOs 3.1 and 3.3) Allow 10 minutes

Have a go at the Stroop task shown below. You will need a stopwatch to time how long it takes to go through the lists naming the colour of the ink in which the word is written.

From Figure 3.7 list the colours down a column before moving to the next column in a left to right direction. For comparison you have two lists, one in which the actual word and ink colour are compatible and one in which they are not always compatible, as is found in a Stroop task. Which one takes you longer? The reaction times that you have recorded are examples of ratio data; to learn more about ratio data and the alternatives, see Box 3.1.

(a)		(b)	
BLUE	YELLOW	**YELLOW**	RED
GREEN	**RED**	GREEN	**GREEN**
RED	BLUE	BLUE	YELLOW
YELLOW	GREEN	RED	**GREEN**
RED	**RED**	YELLOW	BLUE
YELLOW	YELLOW	RED	RED
GREEN	BLUE	GREEN	**YELLOW**
BLUE	GREEN	BLUE	RED
RED	YELLOW	YELLOW	BLUE
GREEN	BLUE	**BLUE**	RED
YELLOW	YELLOW	**GREEN**	BLUE
GREEN	GREEN	BLUE	GREEN
BLUE	**RED**	GREEN	RED
RED	BLUE	**YELLOW**	YELLOW

Figure 3.7 Two lists for use in the Stroop task.

Box 3.1 Research Methods: Types of data

The reaction-time data that you collected for Activity 3.2 is an example of ratio data or the ratio level of measurement. However, data can also be defined as interval, ordinal and nominal (sometimes the latter is also called categorical); so what is the difference between these four levels of measurement or types of data? Ratio measurement is what we tend to think of as 'real measurements' because we can assess precisely the size of differences between the values. For example, if you look ahead to Figure 3.8 and examine the low control group, you can see that the reaction times for the gambling-related list is 737 s whilst it is 712 s for the neutral list. This means we can say that the difference is 25 s. Importantly, in ratio data the value of zero is absolute, meaning that there is a complete absence of the thing being measured. In this case, reaction time can be zero if a person (or animal) has no reaction. With ratio measurements, values can also be compared as multiples of one another allowing for statements such as person A reacted twice as fast as person B. Interval measurements are similar to ratio data in that the values form a scale in which points are equidistant from each other. However, unlike ratio data the values cannot be compared in multiples and the value of zero is not absolute. A typical example of interval data is the Celsius scale of temperature measurement. Although there is a value of zero degrees Celsius on this scale this value does not reflect a complete absence of heat and so the scale is an interval scale rather than a ratio scale.

Both ratio and interval data measure quantities and therefore can be referred to as quantitative. By contrast, with ordinal data it is possible to rank the data but not to assess the differences between them. For example, if you are investigating the level of contact parents had with their small children, you might have a rating scale of (1) no contact; (2) hand contact; (3) carrying. The final type of data is nominal data in which you can categorise the variable but you cannot rank the categories. For example, you might want to investigate people's professions and you can categorise them according to their work, but these cannot be ranked. When you are looking at data or collecting your own, it is important to be aware of which type of data you are working with, as this will affect the type of analysis you might do and what conclusions you can make.

The Stroop task is used to provide an indirect measure of attention and therefore any attention biases, because it is assumed that attending to the meaning of the word interferes with saying the colour of the print. Now you have seen how the Stroop task works, can you guess how it might be modified in order to determine whether addicted individuals are biased towards addiction-related stimuli?

One way would be to substitute some of the words for those that either relate to the addiction or are neutral with respect to it. If an addicted individual displays an attention bias, you would expect that the addiction-related words would distract the participant more than the neutral words and thus result in a longer time being taken to name the colours for the list containing addiction-related words. Neutral words might include items such as fireplace, chair, cupboard, whilst addiction-related words could include needle, relapse and dealer. One important consideration is that the neutral and addiction-related words should be of similar length, number of syllables and frequency in the language.

- Why is this important?

- By matching the different lists for these criteria, the experimenter can assume that any differences are due to the semantics or meaning of the words rather than ease and speed of reading or familiarity.

There is evidence from a number of drug addictions that addicted individuals do perform slower on the lists that contain addiction-related words, implying an attention bias to these words (Field and Cox, 2008). More recently, similar evidence has been found for gambling, as shown in Figure 3.8.

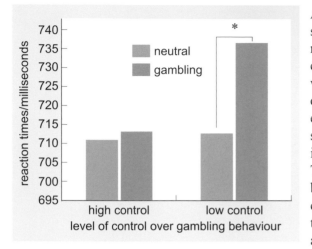

Figure 3.8 Reaction times from a modified Stroop task in gamblers displaying either high or low control over their gambling. Those showing low control (akin to being addicted rather than engaging in controlled use) performed slower when the Stroop task included gambling-related words. Data from Boyer and Dickerson (2003).

As well as establishing that addicted individuals perform slower on these modified tests, psychologists have offered a number of explanations as to why this might happen. The most commonly cited reason is simply that the addiction-related words undergo automatic processing of meaning which slows down the naming of the colour. However, there are other explanations such as that put forward by Tiffany (1990) who suggested that the presentation of an addiction-related word induces craving and effectively causes a cognitive go-slow. This is not necessarily at odds with the idea of an attention bias because it is widely accepted that attention bias and craving have a mutually excitatory relationship. This means that when an addiction-related stimulus is presented, the attention bias causes the individual to focus on it, which in turn induces craving. Reciprocally, the craving increases the attention bias and so forth.

More recently, Klein (2007) proposed that the slowness was due to the cognitive effort of addicted individuals to suppress their thoughts on their addiction when presented with such stimuli. Klein tested this by conducting the modified Stroop task with two groups of individuals addicted to alcohol. The first group were instructed to suppress their thoughts of alcohol, whilst the second group were told they could freely experience any alcohol-related thoughts. The latter group showed no Stroop effect, suggesting that attempts to suppress the thoughts of their addiction contribute to the slowed reaction times.

Having established that biases exist and that they may be due to attempts by addicted individuals to suppress addiction-related thoughts or due to craving, we now need to take a step back and ask how such biases might develop. There are a variety of ideas about how this could happen, beginning with the theory that they develop through classical conditioning. An example of this would be where an initially neutral stimulus commonly associated with the addiction (such as a syringe) becomes a conditional stimulus following repeated associations with the unconditional stimulus, in this case the drug. However, in a model of addiction, is classical conditioning sufficient for explaining the development of the complex behaviour? Field and Cox (2008) suggest that it is not quite sufficient and that this classical conditioning must combine with craving such that the conditioning causes individuals to experience craving following presentation of the previously neutral stimulus, which in turn induces an attention bias and, as outlined above, the two have a positive feedback relationship such that craving increases bias and vice versa. They suggest that this process of a continuous build-up of craving and bias is influenced by an individual's impulsivity and behavioural control, as well as their conscious efforts to suppress craving.

To summarise, the cognitive bias model posits that through a process of classical conditioning and craving, attention biases develop that drive addictive behaviour. These biases have been found consistently in drug and behavioural addictions using the Stroop task. Moreover, the development and maintenance of these biases are influenced by individual traits.

Evaluating the cognitive bias model

Before we return to our four criteria to evaluate this model of addiction, take a few minutes to evaluate the model yourself and fill in the table from Activity 3.1.

Firstly, does the model explain how addiction arises and is maintained? This model suggests that compulsion arises as a result of attention biases that have developed through classical conditioning combining with craving. The mutually excitatory relationship between the biases and craving could also explain maintenance.

Secondly, does the model explain the observed features of addiction? The model explains cue-induced craving but does not deal with tolerance or withdrawal.

Thirdly, does the model explain individual differences in addiction development? As with a number of the previous models, this suggests a role for impulsivity as well as conscious attempts at control, which can vary with individuals.

Finally, does the model make any predictions about treatments? The model does not make any explicit suggestions about treatment, but given the reciprocity of craving and attention bias, it follows that any treatment that can reduce craving could also reduce bias and therefore increase the chances of abstinence. Indeed, Stroop task results have been shown to be predictive of treatment outcome in individuals addicted to heroin (Marissen et al., 2006), with those showing reduced attention bias having more success in treatment.

Now that you have evaluated some psychological models of addiction, how do you think they relate to the biomedical models discussed in Section 3.2? One thing that you might have noticed is that the two types of models tend to explain things at different levels. The biomedical models tend to put the explanation at the level of the biology of the individual whilst the psychological models work at the level of behaviour and choice. Therefore the two types of model are not mutually exclusive. For example, the attention bias may develop in a way that involves changes in dopamine sensitivity, as suggested in the incentive sensitisation model.

3.4 Sociological and demographic factors affecting addiction

As you saw in Section 1.3, various other factors such as the social context and demographic characteristics can affect addiction, such as life events, gender and availability of a drug. Unlike in the previous sections, we will not look at any one model but rather examine the evidence that such factors do

You met demographic factors in Book 2, Section 4.2.4.

impact on addiction. As we do so, we will also discuss how these social factors might influence the psychology and biology of the individual as we move towards a multifactor model of addiction.

3.4.1 Life events

You will recall from Section 3.2.1 that family, adoption and twin studies have revealed information about genetic contributions to addiction, but in doing so, they have also highlighted a role for environmental factors, particularly parental divorce and mental health problems, which influence the development of drug addiction (Agrawal and Lynskey, 2008). Indeed a number of life events have been found to increase the risk of drug addiction including:

- loss of parent
- isolation and abandonment
- loss of child by death or removal
- unfaithfulness of significant other
- loss of home in natural disaster
- death of significant other/close relative
- victim or observer of violent act
- physical, sexual or emotional trauma or neglect.

You may well have noticed that this list bears some resemblance to the life events discussed in Book 2, Section 2.2.2.

■ From your knowledge gained in Book 2, and considering the opponent motivational process model and the assignment example, how might the stress system be affected by these events?

☐ All of these events are major stressors and so it is probable that the stress response will be severe and prolonged.

It is likely that all of these events will act as acute, if not chronic, stressors and, as such, can impact significantly on the body's stress systems, which could lead to changes in the brain that increase the probability of engaging in particular behaviours. For example, a prolonged stress response can sensitise the brain's dopamine system. Research has repeatedly shown that stress increases self-administration of drugs in animals and can trigger relapse in abstinent addicted individuals. The latter is thought to be due to stress activating an already sensitised dopamine system.

■ What psychological factors might affect how someone copes with any of these situations?

☐ Some people might be better at coping than others or be more optimistic (Book 2, Section 2.2.5) and this might help reduce the impact such events have on their life. By contrast, someone who does not cope well or is perhaps more prone to worrying about things will find these events much harder to cope with. How an individual appraises the situation will also have an impact (Book 2, Section 2.2.4).

If someone finds a particular event or situation difficult to cope with they may experience a negative mood, for which they seek a cure through drugs or potentially addictive behaviours.

3.4.2 Age

In addition to the life events, particular age groups are thought to be more at risk of developing addiction. For example, much of the anti-drugs literature is commonly targeted at adolescents, with the advocates of these approaches believing that this age range are particularly at risk.

- Can you think why this age group might be especially at risk of becoming addicted?

- Adolescence is a very stressful time when individuals may feel extremely self-conscious and wish to belong to a group, which makes them vulnerable. It is also a period associated with strong peer-pressure.

Psychologists believe that the high vulnerability in adolescence is not specific to developing addictions but rather is due to people of this age having greater impulsivity and increased novelty-seeking behaviour in general. In terms of drug-taking, this is reflected in adolescents not only being more sensitive to the positive effects of the drugs but also being less sensitive to the negative effects when compared to adults, both of which may add to the increased drug-taking behaviour. Experiments in rodents have compared adolescents and adults and have shown that adolescents learn how to acquire drugs quicker and maintain the behaviour for longer. Figure 3.9 shows data from a study that investigated, not only the rate of acquisition for adolescent and adult rats, but also considered gender as an additional variable.

- From the figure, work out how many daily sessions are required before the percentage of male adolescent and adult rats acquiring the behaviour reaches its maximum; what is the maximum?

- 100% of the adolescent male rats acquire the behaviour by day 6, whilst the adults reach a maximum of 75% acquiring the behaviour at day 11.

In addition to the psychosocial reasons why adolescents may be more vulnerable, scientists have put forward two neurobiological reasons for this increased vulnerability. The first is the incentive motivation pathway, which is more active during adolescence, which might serve to increase the reinforcing nature of drugs or particular behaviours as well as impulsivity (Chambers et al., 2003). This is combined with the second factor: slower maturation of the prefrontal cortex. This brain region is involved in self-regulating behaviour, effectively stopping an individual acting on every impulse and urge they have. Thus the differential activity of these two systems combines to put adolescents in the precarious position of having poor judgement and lack of impulse control even as they are driven to seek increasing levels of novelty and external stimulation.

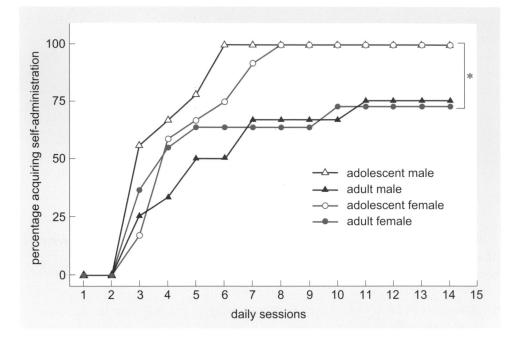

Figure 3.9 Percentage of rats acquiring amphetamine self-administration over daily sessions, with infusion amphetamine available to adolescent and adult, male and female rats. The term 'acquiring self-administration' can be taken to mean the time taken to learn that lever pressing in a chamber similar to the Skinner box will result in direct administration of the drug. Data taken from Shahbazi et al. (2008).

3.4.3 Social status

Research in monkeys (Morgan et al., 2002) has suggested that the social status of a monkey is directly related to how reinforcing a drug is perceived to be, and therefore the likelihood of increasing use. When monkeys were socially housed, the number of dopamine receptors increased, but only in the dominant monkeys; the number remained the same in subordinates. When later tested on the reinforcing effects of cocaine, the subordinates found the drug to be more reinforcing and therefore were at increased risk to repeat and escalate use. Presumably this was because in the higher-status monkey, the number of dopamine receptors meant that high levels of dopamine could normally bind to them. In contrast, in the lower-status monkeys, it is likely that very little dopamine normally bound to the receptors before it was removed from the synapse and therefore the presence of cocaine made a substantial difference to the binding levels by keeping the dopamine at the synapse for longer. This raises the possibility that the social status of an individual can influence the probability of engaging in drug-taking behaviours. It also demonstrates the ability of the environment to alter receptor numbers. However, the social status of a monkey is subject to fewer confines than that of a human.

Indeed research in humans has shown that use of certain drugs can be more prevalent in some socio-economic groups than others. For example, cocaine use in the 1980s and 1990s was considered glamorous and confined to the upper and middle classes. However, as its use became seen as something to be avoided, use of the drug decreased in higher socio-economic status groups and increased in lower socio-economic status groups (Miech and Chilcoat, 2007). In addition to this, another study (Smyth and O'Brien, 2004) suggests that child heroin users, in particular, are more likely to be homeless and, as such, of a lower socio-economic group. Therefore the results from human studies are both variable and attributable to factors that are not easily transferable to animal studies. Add to this the fact that social status may change as a consequence of addiction and the problems associated with it, and we see that research in this area is fraught with difficulties.

3.4.4 Gender

Data from animal studies suggest that there are sex differences in the responses to addictive drugs. Females have been shown to be more sensitive to the positive effects of drugs whilst males are more sensitive to the negative effects (Carroll et al., 2009) and, accordingly, it is thought that females are more vulnerable to developing addiction as they are more likely to experience positive reinforcement. However, once addicted, males may suffer more from withdrawal and therefore maintain drug use to prevent the negative effects. These results are supported by studies in humans, with reports of a heightening drug high and wanting at particular points in the menstrual cycle and research suggesting that oestrogen facilitates drug abuse (Carroll et al., 2009).

3.4.5 Prior exposure to other drugs

For the sake of completeness, we shall also consider the idea of previous exposure to one drug increasing the risk of developing addiction to another drug as an environmental risk factor - the **gateway effect**. This term is normally used when talking about the use of a drug such as cannabis increasing later use of a drug like heroin. In the media, the terms 'soft' and 'hard' drugs might be used, respectively. However, within scientific literature these terms are avoided as their basis is controversial: for example, with soft drugs having connotations of safety and insignificant harm. The use of a drug like cannabis is generally thought to be associated with lesser criminality than a drug such as heroin but none the less can provide the individual with a gateway to availability of heroin.

What evidence is there then for a gateway effect? Human studies have shown, with some consistency, that use of cannabis, and in some instances ecstasy, typically precedes use of other illicit drugs such as cocaine and heroin, and that the earlier and the more regularly cannabis is used, the more likely the individual is to use these other drugs. Three explanations are made for this gateway effect. Firstly, it is suggested that the increased likelihood of use of other drugs following cannabis use is due to a shared illicit market for the drugs; that is, the cannabis user simply has better access to other drugs, a claim often used in favour of greater legal differentiation between cannabis and other drugs. Secondly, it is suggested that the increase is merely due to the characteristics of a cannabis user; that is, the person who is more likely to take cannabis is also more likely to take heroin. Both of these explanations are non-causal in that they do not suggest use of cannabis *causes* use of other drugs. The final explanation is that the pharmacological effects of cannabis cause an increase in the individual's propensity to use other drugs and is therefore a causal explanation.

Evidence for causality is unsurprisingly lacking in human data; indeed it would be extremely difficult to conduct a practical and ethical investigation into this matter in humans. However, animal studies may offer some insight into whether a causal relationship is likely. Certainly, it is known that all addictive drugs including cannabis act on the dopamine system. In addition to this, it has been shown that treatment with the active ingredient of cannabis can enhance motor or physical activity in response to amphetamine and heroin. These motor responses also depend on dopamine levels, albeit elsewhere in the brain, therefore suggesting some positive interaction. Interestingly, these enhancements were limited to a group of 'high-responder' rats, a particular strain prone to addictive behaviours. Although this does provide some evidence for cannabis use altering subsequent responses to other drugs, indicative of a causal link, the findings were for the movement or locomotor effects of amphetamine and heroin, rather than the rewarding effects, which are more closely linked to repeated drug use and development of addiction. Therefore, before any firm conclusions from the field of neurobiology can be made regarding the causal nature of the gateway effect, further studies are required that examine the effects of cannabis on both the rewarding effects of other drugs and the transition to addiction to these drugs. At present there is no research into the gateway effect for addictive behaviours.

To summarise, there is considerable evidence that a variety of sociological and demographic factors can affect addiction. Therefore a truly comprehensive model of addiction should consider these influences in addition to biological and psychological factors.

3.5 Towards an integrated model of addiction

3.5.1 The excessive appetites model

You have now read about two broad classes of model; those that take the biomedical approach and those that focus on psychological factors. In addition, you have seen that there are a variety of sociological and demographic factors that might affect addiction. Take a few minutes to look back over your table for Activity 3.1. You should see that there are merits and drawbacks to each of the models and that no model also takes into account all additional sociological and demographic factors. Moreover, the focus of most of these models has been on addictions to drugs rather than behaviours. This is largely due to the available evidence but of course a suitable model should be able to account for all addictions. Therefore in order to best model addiction, it is important to attempt to combine different factors, drawing on the strong points of a variety of models with the view to creating a model that can serve both drug and behavioural addictions. One of the most successful attempts at this was developed by Orford (2001) who combined psychological and social factors to derive the psychosocial model of addiction referred to as the excessive appetites model.

This model proposes that a number of appetitive activities exist to which it is possible to become addicted. These can include drugs such as heroin but can also include behaviours such as eating and sex. Orford suggests that how much someone engages with the appetitive activity can be determined by a number of factors.

■ Have a think back over the psychological and social factors that you have learnt about; what kind of factors might affect how much someone engages with these appetitive activities?

☐ You could have come up with all sorts of answers here, such as their personality, perhaps their level of impulsiveness or the behaviour of their peers.

Indeed Orford proposed a number of determinants including personality, availability, influence of friends' behaviour and opinions. He suggests that once an individual has engaged with an appetitive activity, the transition to compulsion can happen through a combination of drive for positive incentive and removal of negative conditions, learning and coping, as well as developing an attachment to the behaviour. He suggests that the activity and associated stimuli gain salience which can bias attention and memory.

Through these processes, consumption can increase in the absence of significant environmental or physiological constraints until addiction develops.

■ Can you think of an environmental and physiological constraint to developing alcoholism?

☐ An environmental constraint may be availability of alcohol, whilst a physiological constraint might be the physical ill-health caused by elevated levels of alcohol, which varies between individuals such that some are known to experience negative after-effects which are more severe and last longer than others.

Once developed, addiction may then be maintained as a consequence of negative feelings and a sense of hopelessness, as well as through processes of neuro-adaptation.

The latter may surprise you as this model is not touted as a biomedical model. Indeed, although Orford did not believe that addiction was a disease, as the original biomedical models did, he does believe that biological factors should come into play at various points, such as through reward processing or neuro-adaptation.

Neuro-adaption is another term for plasticity (Book 1, Section 2.2.2).

The excessive appetites model also makes some specific predictions about how addicted individuals could recover from their addiction, stating that there are two stages to this process. The first is a decision or resolution to change by the individual, which is likely to be due to conflicts that arise both within the individual and around them that are caused by the addiction. For example, the conflict that might arise between one's family and addiction. The second stage that Orford proposes is a behavioural stage, or simply acting on the decision to stop an addiction.

Evaluating the excessive appetites model

We can now return to our four criteria for the final time and consider how the excessive appetites model stands up to them, but before we do so, take a few minutes to evaluate the model yourself.

Firstly, does this model explain how addiction develops and is maintained? Yes, the model does offer some idea of how the behaviour may lead to addiction by suggesting that a combination of increased desire, decreased restraint and attachment are important. Addiction can then be maintained through feelings of negative affect and hopelessness as well as neuroadaptation.

Secondly, can the model explain the features of addiction such as craving, tolerance and withdrawal? Given that the model integrates psychological and sociological factors, it can account for the same features as psychological models. For example, the strong attachment to the behaviour could increase saliency and therefore may account for craving. Although psychosocial factors do not account well for withdrawal and tolerance, the concession that some neuroadaptation might occur could allow these to be explained through opponent processes.

Thirdly, can the model explain the individual differences in development of addiction? The model allows for a vast number and variety of influences to impact on behaviour and so it can account for the individual differences seen in addiction by virtue of different people being affected differently by the various biopsychosocial influences.

Finally, does the model make any predictions about treatment? The model puts motivation of the addicted individual at the very centre and therefore puts the emphasis on the individual to enact the change. However, unlike the rational choice model, this is not considered to be blaming the addicted individual for their addiction because the model acknowledges that the addiction can be influenced by a variety of factors, some of which may be beyond the individual's control. In addition, any way to decrease the influence of factors likely to increase addictive behaviour would be supported by this model, for example decreasing stress.

3.6 A biopsychosocial approach to addiction

We have now reviewed a variety of models, each with a different emphasis; from those that focused only on the biology to others that made little mention of it. From your table you should have noticed that each of the models accounts for particular criteria better than others but that any model that focuses solely on the biological or psychological cannot provide a fully comprehensive model. The excessive appetites model, which can be considered a psychosocial model, however, does provide a reasonably comprehensive set of influences that may explain addiction. Although Orford made the point of stating that this model was not biomedical, he also acknowledged that biology is likely to have an effect on addiction and therefore his model is perhaps a little more than a psychosocial model. Indeed it could be regarded as heading towards a biopsychosocial approach.

To illustrate the worth of such an approach, consider what your table would look like if you combined the information on the excessive appetites model with the information on the biomedical models – the result is likely to be quite convincing and able to explain more about addiction than a less inclusive model. This biopsychosocial approach provides a framework in which a variety of factors can affect addiction and those that affect one time point in addiction may differ from those at a different time point: for example, the development of addiction may be influenced by factors that are different from those that influence the maintenance of addiction.

By using such an approach it is possible to see factors on a variety of levels, effectively explaining or describing the same thing in multiple ways. For example, consider the idea that there is an increased wanting for the drug or behaviour which underlies the development of addiction. This increased wanting could be labelled as a psychological factor, but if you look back to the model of incentive sensitisation, it is suggested that the increased wanting is caused by changes in the mesolimbocortical pathway, so is this a biological factor? Likewise, a stressful life event can be considered a sociological factor but it is also the individual's reaction to the event and how they cope with it that will determine the effect of that event and this might be considered a psychological factor. Moreover, you have seen in Books 1 and 2 that there are specific biological processes associated with stress, meaning stress can be interpreted as sociological, psychological and biological.

As well as categorising factors as being biological, psychological or sociological, they can be considered in terms of their type and level of influence. Petraitis et al. did just this in 1995 for experimental drug use and concluded that there are three types of influence acting at three different levels. These are summarised in Figure 3.10. The three different types of influence are social/interpersonal, cultural/attitudinal and intrapersonal. These influences can act at different levels, with proximal factors being most likely to have an immediate effect on use and distal and ultimate factors having less immediate impact but none the less contributing to long-term risk. You will see in the figure that biological, psychological and sociological factors are all involved in the decision to experiment with drugs and can all be classified as proximal, distal and ultimate. The proximal factors are those that have a direct influence, whilst ultimate factors are not thought to have a direct role in the decision to take drugs and distal factors are defined as being between these two levels.

The biopsychosocial approach, therefore, not only allows all types of factors to be considered but also acknowledges the proximity of their influence. This integrative approach permits addiction to be viewed from the standpoints of multiple models, meaning that the strengths and evidence for all models can be taken into account when studying and treating addiction.

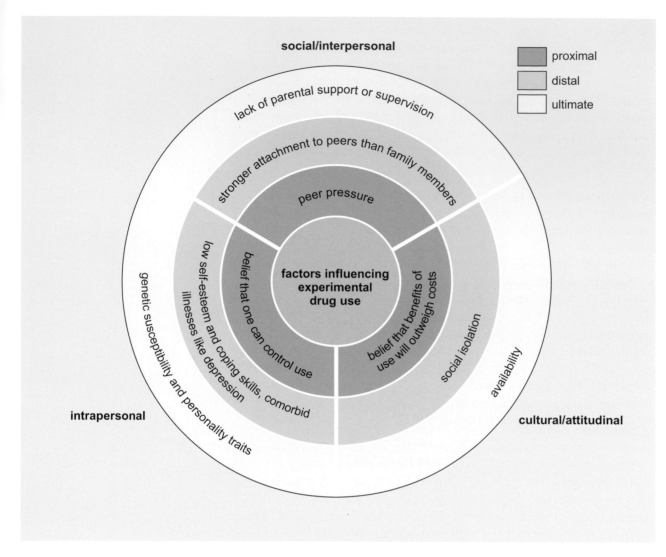

Figure 3.10 The different types and levels of influence of factors on experimental drug use. Adapted from Petraitis et al. (1995).

3.7 Final word

In this chapter you have learnt about a number of different models for addiction. These models range from the idea that addiction develops as a result of a rational choice to the suggestion that addiction is strongly genetic and not a result of choice. However, as you evaluated these models it should have become apparent that no single model can be considered ideal, with each having different strengths and weaknesses. Through this process of evaluation, a biopsychosocial approach to addiction emerges to allow a variety of factors to influence addiction at differing levels. In the following chapter we will examine how addiction might be treated. In doing this, you will need to keep in mind the different models and, of course, the biopsychosocial approach to addiction.

3.8 Summary of Chapter 3

- There are a number of models of addiction but these models are not mutually exclusive.
- Each of these models meets the four criteria for a model of addiction with differing levels of success.
- By combining influential factors, more convincing models can be developed such as the psychosocial excessive appetites model.
- The gold standard for modelling addiction is a model that includes biological, psychological and social factors and gives some indication of the magnitude of effect of these factors – the biopsychosocial approach.

3.9 Learning outcomes

LO 3.1 Describe the different models of addiction and evaluate them using appropriate criteria. (KU1, KU2, KU3, CS5)

LO 3.2 Recognise and interpret a variety of evidence in support of or against these different models. (KU5, CS4)

LO 3.3 Show that you understand the limitations of the methods used to investigate addiction. (KU5, CS4)

LO 3.4 Identify and explain how certain factors may increase the risk of becoming addicted and the consequences such knowledge may have for the individual, community and wider society. (KU3, CS5)

3.10 Self-assessment questions

SAQ 3.1 (LO 3.1)

Explain the role of dopamine in the two exposure models of addiction.

SAQ 3.2 (LO 3.1)

Ravi is recovering from heroin addiction and last used the drug four years ago. He says that moving away from where he used to live has really helped him to control his craving. Can you explain why this might be?

SAQ 3.3 (LO 3.3)

For each of the following research strategies provide one limitation of the method for investigating addiction:

(a) family studies
(b) self-report
(c) animal studies.

SAQ 3.4 (LOs 3.1 and 3.4)

Explain why an individual who has an addiction may be more likely to relapse during periods of intense stress.

SAQ 3.5 (LO 3.4)

If researchers wanted to mimic the vulnerability factors of adolescence in a mouse, what sort of things might they look for?

SAQ 3.6 (LO 3.4)

What might be the implications of knowledge that addictions are more likely to develop in those of a particular social status?

Chapter 4   Treating addiction

Eleanor Dommett

4.1   Types of treatment

Through the course of this book you have learnt how addiction can develop to a variety of drugs and behaviours, but that, whatever the object of the addiction, a number of core characteristics are found. One of the most important of these in terms of treating addiction is the chronic, relapsing nature of the problem. When dealing with a chronic health problem, there are generally two approaches available. If the problem is preventable in some way, intervention can begin before the onset of the problem. For example, health care professionals may campaign or intervene to reduce the number of individuals starting the problem behaviour or drug use in the first place. Therefore the first type of intervention that forms part of addiction treatment is aimed at **prevention**.

In addition to the interventions aimed at decreasing development of addiction, there are also treatments aimed at stopping the addiction once it has developed. These types of intervention are referred to as **cessation** treatments.

It is important to recognise that these two approaches can be used for both physical and mental health problems. For example, a doctor may prescribe statins to reduce cholesterol level and recommend that an individual takes exercise and maintains a healthy diet to prevent heart disease. However, if the individual then suffers from angina or a heart attack, they may then be given a surgical treatment such as an angioplasty to widen the arteries in the heart and effectively stop the problem; that is, a cessation treatment.

4.2   General issues in prevention treatments

An intervention aimed at preventing a health problem arising can take place either before onset of the behaviour or before the behaviour reaches damaging levels.

- ■   Using alcohol as an example, can you think of when these two time points might be?

- ☐   The first time point might be before the individual starts drinking alcohol at all, whilst the second might be when they are drinking but in a controlled manner.

These time points can be the same for a variety of health problems and the aim is to prevent potentially damaging behaviours starting and then preventing permanent damage occurring once the behaviour has been initiated.

As well as the time point at which a prevention intervention starts, it is important to consider what the focus of the intervention will be. In the previous chapters you have learnt that all addictions share common features and that addiction *per se* rather than specific addictions appear to be at least in part heritable (Section 3.2.1). Therefore, one question that needs to be addressed is whether interventions should be aimed at specific addictions or rather more generally at addictive behaviours.

■ Can you think of an advantage to tailoring a prevention treatment to a specific addiction?

☐ If the intervention is specific, it is likely that the individual will find it more relevant and as a result they may feel more supported and therefore more likely to achieve the goal of preventing addiction developing.

■ Can you think of a disadvantage of tailoring a prevention treatment to a specific addiction?

☐ This could reduce the number of people the intervention is relevant to, making it less economical to run.

In addition, you may recall the example of Gary in Activity 1.1, who had a number of addictions. This is not uncommon. Therefore if someone has multiple addictions and switches between them, a narrow treatment intervention is likely to be less useful.

More general interventions are often harder to finance because much of the addiction treatment available is led by charities that are dedicated to battling particular addictions and therefore wish to provide tailored treatments. Johnson et al. (1996) evaluated the effectiveness of three different breadths of intervention on the percentage of youths smoking. Figure 4.1 shows summary data from a number of different studies, grouped into smoking-specific, multiple-substance and lifestyle intervention programmes.

■ Put these three types of intervention in order from the most specific to the broadest.

☐ Smoking-specific, multiple-substance and finally lifestyle (broadest).

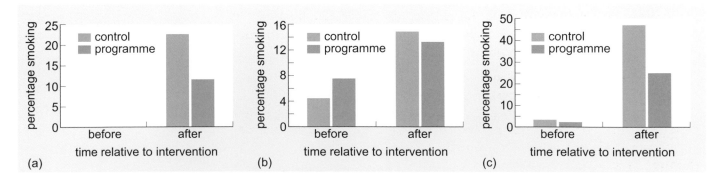

Figure 4.1 The effect of different intervention programmes on the percentage of youths smoking: (a) smoking-specific intervention; (b) multiple-substance intervention; and (c) lifestyle intervention. Data adapted from Johnson et al. (1996).

- Describe the effects of the smoking-specific intervention on smoking level. Note that the control group would have had control intervention/ workshops.

☐ Before the interventions none of the participants smoked. After the intervention approximately 22.5% of those in the control condition smoked whilst around 12% of those in the smoking-specific intervention group smoked.

The lack of smokers prior to the smoking-specific intervention is likely to be due to these schemes targeting young people before they start smoking. Therefore, in this instance, the important data for comparison is the percentages smoking after the intervention relative to the control group. From this it is clear that those who had undergone the smoking-specific intervention were about half as likely to smoke as those who had not.

The results from the multiple-substance intervention appear to be similar for the control and experimental interventions, with only about 2% difference between the two groups. However, in this instance there were smokers in the groups before the intervention and so it is possible to look at the change between the before and after measures.

- How did the percentage of smokers change in the two groups, before and after intervention? Do you think the intervention was effective now?

☐ In the control condition the percentage rose from around 4.5% to 15% after the intervention. This is roughly a threefold increase in smokers. In the experimental condition the percentage of smokers rose from around 7.5% to 13% which is about a twofold increase. This suggests that although there is still an increase in smokers over this time period, the multiple-substance intervention reduced the size of this increase.

The final type of programme evaluated in Figure 4.1 is a programme that looks to help individuals make general healthy lifestyle choices.

- By using similar comparisons to those you used to evaluate the multiple-substance intervention above, what conclusions can you draw about the ability of lifestyle interventions to reduce smoking levels?

☐ The control group increased smoking from just over 3% to 47%, approximately a 15-fold increase. The experimental group increased smoking from just under 3% to 25%, around an eightfold increase. This suggests that although smoking did increase in both groups, the increase was substantially smaller in the group exposed to the lifestyle intervention.

Although the results presented in Figure 4.1 show that both specific and general interventions can be effective in preventing uptake of behaviours such as smoking in comparison to no intervention, the effectiveness of the different breadths of treatment may vary depending on the precise addiction being addressed.

.1 **Linking models to treatment**

ﬤ 4.3) Allow 45 minutes

〈 your way through this chapter you should complete the final
ﬣe table you started in Activity 3.1 on 'Actual treatments'. If you
treatment is supported by or based on a particular model, write the
treatment in the appropriate row. You may find that you do not
ﬥent for every model or that the treatment is supported by a
ﬡodels and this is fine.

4.3 Types of prevention treatments

In the previous section you learnt that prevention interventions can occur at
two distinct time points: before initiation of a behaviour or before it becomes
a problem. You have also learnt about the different breadths of intervention
that might take place in a prevention programme. In the remainder of this
section we will discuss two examples of prevention treatments that are
currently used.

4.3.1 School-based programmes

School-based prevention programmes allow students to learn about addictive
drugs and (to a lesser extent) behaviours within a school setting. The main
advantage of such programmes is the widespread manner in which they can be
delivered, such that all children under the age of 16 will be 'a captive
audience' to these lessons. In addition, this allows selective targeting of
adolescents who, as you saw in Chapter 3, are one of the most vulnerable
groups.

■   Can you think of a problem with delivering this message only through
    schools?

☐   Not all children will be attending schools and it may be those who are at
    the greatest risk who do not attend these lessons. Moreover, some
    children will actively rebel against information taught in a classroom
    context.

School-based programmes can be classified as (Tobler, 1986):

1   knowledge-only intervention
2   affective-only intervention
3   knowledge + affective intervention
4   peer-based intervention
5   alternative.

The knowledge-only interventions aim to build a negative attitude towards
drugs and addictive behaviours, thus increasing the perceived cost of engaging

with them. The affective-only strategies aim to build self-esteem and self-awareness, working on the assumption that this will reduce subsequent use of addictive drugs and behaviours. You might like to begin filling in your table for Activity 4.1 now by thinking about whether there is any support for a knowledge-only or affective-only strategy in addiction prevention.

The rational choice and excessive appetites models both involve some analysis of the cost versus benefit of taking a drug or behaving in a certain way. By increasing the negative attitudes towards these drugs and behaviours using a knowledge-only strategy, it is plausible that the cost will be considered higher and therefore the probability of using a drug or behaving in a certain way will decrease. The affective-only strategy has support from all the models that assume a role for psychological factors such as self-esteem and stress, and therefore has support from the opponent motivational process, incentive sensitisation and excessive appetites models.

Of course, by combining the two strategies in a knowledge + affective intervention, more influencing factors are affected, thus increasing the probability of impacting on the behaviour or drug use.

Peer-based interventions include teaching refusal skills and social life skills and are normally aimed at 10–15-year-olds. Such social skills training will generally take the form of between five and 20 individual hour-long sessions which cover three main areas. Firstly, basic topics such as listening skills and decision-making are covered. Secondly, peer views of drug use or addictive behaviour are discussed and students are taught refusal techniques. Finally, actual drug use or behaviour in peers is calculated and discussed. Students are encouraged to be open about their views on taking drugs. The aim of such sessions is to demonstrate that peers do not look favourably on such actions, despite perceptions; effectively undermining the peer pressure that may drive students to experiment with drugs or addictive behaviours. Many of these interventions focus heavily on the refusal training element. Indeed, this idea is the basis behind all 'Just Say No' campaigns (Figure 4.2) and it assumes that educating young people to say no to drugs or addictive behaviours will prevent them from engaging with them. However, this refusal training alone may actually be counterproductive because it gives the impression that the use or behaviour is more prevalent than it actually is. Therefore in order to be effective, it needs to be combined with evaluation of drug use in peers.

The final stage involves this calculation of actual drug use in peers and a comparison with estimated drug use.

■ Given that the aim is to prevent socially or peer-driven drug use, can you guess which will be higher: actual or estimated drug use?

□ Estimated use is nearly always higher than actual use as individuals form perceptions that their peers are frequently engaging in such behaviours for example because stories may be exaggerated to gain peer approval; therefore by calculating actual use the students are provided with a more realistic behavioural norm.

Much like the affective-only interventions, peer-based interventions are supported by a number of addiction models including the opponent

Figure 4.2 A 'Just Say No' campaign targeted at adolescents linked to a popular television programme.

motivational process and incentive sensitisation models, assuming that a lack of social skills may be a stressor. In addition, peer-based interventions are supported by models that involve a cost–benefit analysis in which social norms may play a role, and this type of intervention is therefore supported by the excessive appetites and rational choice models.

The final type of school-based intervention comes under the mysterious heading of 'alternative'. This category includes all other interventions, most commonly those encouraging other activities rather than drug use or addictive behaviours (Figure 4.3).

Figure 4.3 School-based intervention.

In order to evaluate the efficacy of these school-based interventions, Faggiano et al. (2008) undertook a meta-analysis (Book 2, Box 1.7) to examine the effects of drugs prevention programmes. They combined the results from 29 different studies, 28 of which were based in the USA and only one in the UK. They found that using skills-based programmes, under the umbrella of peer-based interventions (which aimed to increase abilities in general), refusal and safety skills could reduce drug use by around 20% for cannabis and 55% for drugs considered more addictive, such as heroin.

They also found that whilst knowledge + affective strategies improved drug knowledge and decision-making, it had little effect on actual drug use. Knowledge-only strategies did reliably increase knowledge, although not in a way that altered actual drug use.

Interestingly, the same interventions were more effective when delivered by peers rather than teachers. However, in order to be effective, they do require the support of parents or caregivers as well as wider society to actually be effective.

To summarise, school-based interventions can take a number of forms, but they are generally aimed at increasing students' knowledge and providing them with the social and psychological skills thought to protect against drug use or addictive behaviours. However, to date, most of these have been implemented in the USA and focused on drugs, rather than addictive behaviours.

4.3.2 Legislation-based prevention

The current prohibition approach to the majority of addictive drugs, and controlled access to others and certain behaviours through licensing laws, is essentially a legislation-based prevention scheme. Current laws attempt to limit availability of drugs and potentially addictive behaviours, in the hope that the deterrent of criminal conviction and the effort required to access the drugs or behaviour will prevent most individuals initiating these practices.

There has been little research into whether limiting availability to a drug or behaviour really does limit use in humans and, of course, research into legal status is impossible in non-human animals, where no such equivalent status exists. However, there is evidence from studies in rats to suggest that increasing the availability of the drug will increase the amount ingested (Mantsch et al., 2004), suggesting that limiting availability does limit use. By contrast, Figure 4.4 shows results from human research demonstrating that lifetime cannabis use is lower in the Netherlands, than in some other countries, despite possession and sale of small quantities of the drug being tolerated through a formal non-enforcement policy resulting in *de facto* legalisation. This research indicates that increased availability does not necessarily result in a high number of users (Vega et al., 2002).

The term *de facto* derives from Latin and refers to actual practice that is not necessarily permitted by law.

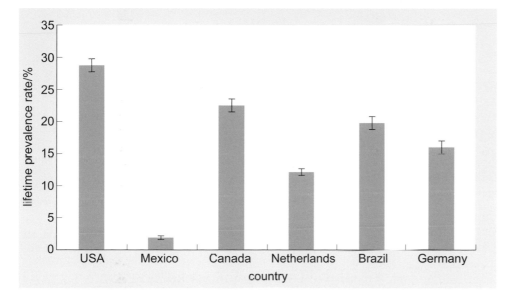

Figure 4.4 Lifetime prevalence rates for cannabis use across six different countries expressed as the percentage of respondents reporting more than five times use. The Netherlands offers the most lenient approach or *de facto* legalisation and yet does not have the highest levels of use. Data adapted from Vega et al. (2002).

■ Identify the countries where cannabis use was the highest and lowest of those studied?

□ The highest use is in the USA and the lowest in Mexico.

On the face of it, these results would therefore suggest that the level of drug use is not dependent on its legal status. However, other research has shown that use of cannabis increased in certain age groups as legal penalties decreased.

■ From your knowledge of risk factors in the previous chapter, what age group would you consider most at risk?

□ The age group when people are considered to be most at risk is adolescence so any age group within this developmental period.

Figure 4.5 shows the prevalence rates for cannabis use in 18–20-year-olds in the Netherlands, USA and Norway between 1984 and 1996. This period is particularly important because it marks the progression from depenalisation (i.e. a reduction in the penalty given) to *de facto* legalisation in the Netherlands.

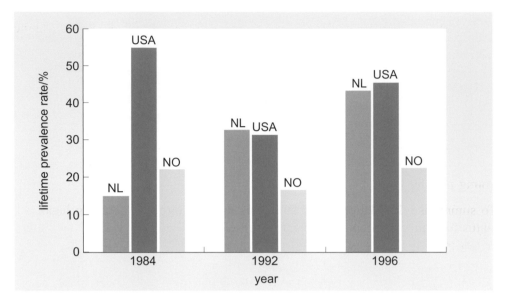

Figure 4.5 Lifetime prevalence rates of 18–20-year-olds in using cannabis between 1984 and 1996 in three countries. During this period the Netherlands (NL) reduced the penalties associated with cannabis use and sale to reach a state of *de facto* legalisation, whilst the USA and Norway (NO) maintained a strict legal stance on the drug. Data adapted from MacCoun and Reuter (1997).

- Looking firstly at the results for the Netherlands alone, what does the pattern suggest about the effect of *de facto* legalisation on use of cannabis in 18–20-year-olds?

☐ Use of the drug increased from 15% to 44% as the legal stance became more lenient.

- Now examine the data for all the countries. Does this data support the conclusion that legalisation increased use in this population? Explain your reasoning.

☐ Although the initial increase between 1984 and 1992 is only found in the Netherlands and therefore could be related to the decreasing legal penalties during this period, the same cannot be said for the period from 1992 to 1996, when all three countries increased use despite differing legal situations.

These results, therefore, suggest that the legal status alone does not define level of use, suggesting that other variables such as individual risk and social factors may be important and unaccounted for with a legislation-based prevention strategy.

Figure 4.6 Example of legally required notices on cigarette packets.

A further attempt to prevent these behaviours is through legally required notices of their negative effects (Figure 4.6). This is most commonly seen with cigarette packets which now carry health warnings. This legal requirement is similar to the knowledge-only strategy in schools in that it aims to increase awareness of the negative effects and therefore create negative attitudes towards smoking.

In addition to strict legislation, suggestions are frequently made to increase the taxes on alcohol and cigarettes and part of the motivation for this is to discourage people from buying them. However, research has shown that increases in the cost of alcohol do not result in a comparable decrease in consumption, assuming that other factors such as income are kept constant (Anderson et al., 2009). That is not to say there is *no* decrease in consumption but that this decrease is smaller than might be expected. Closer examination reveals that increases in price cause those already drinking to switch to a cheaper brand, whilst also slowing progression of alcohol consumption in young people.

To summarise, legislation-based strategies work in three ways: using legal status to reduce availability and increase penalty of use; increasing knowledge of negative effects by legally required notices; and decreasing use by increasing financial cost. However, the two latter approaches are only available for legal drugs or addictive behaviours, meaning that there are a substantial number of addictions that cannot be influenced using these strategies. It could therefore be argued that, should other drugs be made legal, then this approach could be used. However, such a debate requires many factors to be considered and is beyond the scope of SDK228! Although the use of legislation-based strategies is not directly based on any model of addiction, it could be supported by the rational choice and excessive appetites models as both allow for a cost–benefit analysis in which legal cost would be considered.

4.4 The limitations and problems with prevention treatments

In the preceding section you learnt about two main types of prevention strategy. Both strategies aim to impact on social factors that influence use of addictive drugs and behaviours, such as availability and peer pressure. Both also attempt to educate about the negative effects of such drugs and behaviour. However, there are clear limitations to these schemes. Firstly, you saw in Section 4.2.1 that school-based interventions are predominantly found in the USA and are therefore not readily available in other countries. Moreover, for the strategy to be effective it must incorporate a number of different features, such as skills and refusal training. Secondly, legislation-based strategies, although likely to be important, have limited applicability to illegal drugs where controls on notifications of negative effects and cost cannot be applied. Furthermore, such a focused approach alone would not address many of the key factors affecting addiction that were discussed in Chapter 3.

You will also have noticed that there is very little information on the effectiveness of these schemes for addiction to behaviours such as gambling, largely due to a lack of implementation of such strategies in this field. Almost certainly, legislation-based approaches would be impossible for addictions such as workaholism where the subject of the addiction cannot be controlled legally.

In addition to the lack of focus on behavioural addictions, school-based strategies specifically target adolescents, as this age group is known to be at risk; however, as you will recall from Chapter 3, there are a great variety of risk factors identified in all the models, which are not being targeted with these interventions. For example, currently there are no intervention strategies specifically targeting those who are genetically at risk, such as relatives of addicted individuals. Likewise, interventions are not specifically aimed at people who have experienced major stressors, despite this group being at risk. Given the difficulties of applying prevention treatments to all types of addictions and the multiple risk factors, it is perhaps unsurprising that most treatment is in the form of cessation treatment, which is discussed in the following section.

4.5 General issues in cessation treatments

Cessation treatments are aimed at stopping the addicted individual using their drug or engaging in their behaviour of choice. These cessation treatments were for a long time associated purely with stopping the person addicted to alcohol drinking every day or getting the individual addicted to heroin through the 'cold turkey' period. However, it has now been recognised that cessation treatments must consider long-term abstinence, meaning treatment must work beyond the initial detoxification, during which the drug or behaviour is initially removed from the person; there must also be some element of relapse prevention treatment for addiction.

Although addiction cessation may be achieved by the individual alone, it is often the case that they will work towards abstinence through an enrolled programme, which may have both psychosocial and pharmacological elements. Such programmes can be entered into for a variety of reasons. Entry may be through the choice of the addicted individual, following a referral from their GP or through the demand of those around them, both family members and employers. Whilst the reasoning of family members may be clear, it is perhaps less clear why employers may insist upon entry to a programme. To give you an overview of why employers might demand entry, Box 4.1 shows the effects of addiction on employment. Additionally, entry may be legally required: for example, as a condition of early release from prison or instead of a prison sentence.

> **Box 4.1 Addiction and the workplace**
>
> Most organisations now have in place specific guidelines on dealing with employees who have addictions, much as they would for other types of illnesses. This is largely because addiction significantly impacts on an individual's ability to work: for example, around 40% of people with drug problems will be regularly absent from work and when they are able to work, 40% will arrive late and 25% will have problems completing work. Twenty-five per cent will have problems with their

boss and 10% are likely to suffer on-the-job injuries, costing the employer further time and money.

The effects of these work-related problems do not just cost the employer time and money; they may also come at a cost to other employees. For example, other members of staff may have to work harder to compensate and may resent having to do so, creating a hostile working environment.

In addition to these effects relating to the addicted person's employment, those who are in a position of caring for an addicted individual, perhaps a family member, may also find it difficult to work. The main problem here is that whilst the employer may strongly suggest that an addicted individual in their employment should enrol on a programme, this is harder to do if their employee whose performance has been compromised is not the person with the addiction and guidelines are less clear-cut on such an area.

Despite all the different routes through which people may enter programmes and therefore the significant variation in delivery of the intervention, most programmes include some element of education and counselling as well as regular drugs testing. Unlike prevention treatments, whilst cessation interventions may utilise psychosocial techniques, they may also use pharmacological treatments.

Activity 4.2 Routes out of addiction

(LOs 4.2 and 4.3) Allow 20 minutes

Now would be a good time to go to Activity 4.2 where you will watch a brief video in which some of the addicted individuals you met in Chapter 1 talk about how they broke away from their addiction.

4.6 Types of cessation treatment

In this section you will learn about a number of different cessation treatments, ranging from pharmacological treatments to hypnotherapy. As you work through the section, keep in mind the fact that an individual may have more than one type of treatment.

4.6.1 Psychosocial interventions towards cessation

In the previous chapter you learnt about the cognitive bias model of addiction and the implications of this model for treatment will be discussed shortly. However, first another model must be introduced, which specifically focuses on recovery from addiction, rather than its development, and as such was not discussed in Chapter 3. The **transtheoretical model (TTM)** or stages of change model states that with regard to chronic behavioural patterns such as addiction, the behaviour during recovery can be characterised as belonging to one of five stages. This model was developed in the 1980s by Prochaska and DiClemente (1983), and continues to have a significant following in clinical practice. It assumes that the different stages depict motivations of the individual. The different stages and relevant actions and goals at each stage are shown in Figure 4.7.

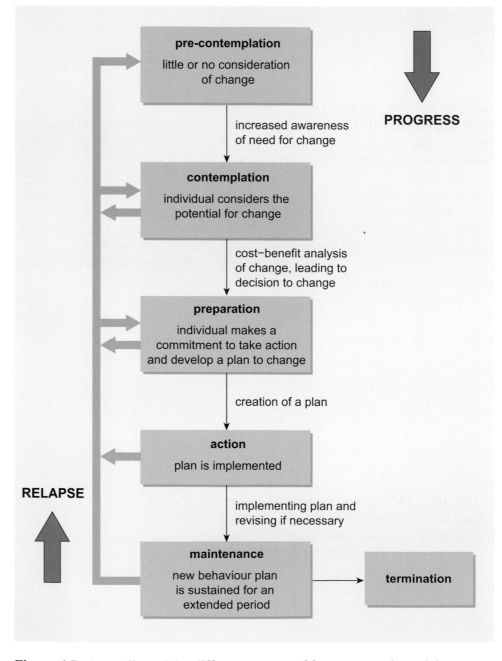

Figure 4.7 An outline of the different stages and how progression might occur according to the transtheoretical or stages of change model of addiction recovery. Data adapted from DiClemente (2003).

The first thing you might notice about the model is the apparent straightforward progression between the different stages. This will no doubt stand in contrast in your mind to the stories of Robin and the other addicted individuals who you met in Activities 1.1 and 4.2. They reported trying to give up their addictions on a number of occasions and failing to do so. According to this model, Robin, for example, must have reached the preparation stage, if not the action stage, and yet he often returned to using heroin. However, the model allows for an individual to move in return to a previous stage and assumes that the behavioural change is unlikely to occur immediately by progression through all stages, but rather a cyclical route is probable, as indicated by the coloured arrows in Figure 4.7.

Movement between the stages may occur due to a variety of reasons. For example, a smoker may move from pre-contemplation to contemplation after being diagnosed with a heart condition such as angina. However, external pressures or consequences are not the only way to progress to contemplation. For example, the model suggests that problem recognition is a key element in the progression and that this problem identification can be supported by health practitioners; medical guidelines in the USA require doctors to ask all patients about smoking and advise them to stop if they are smokers (Anczak and Nogler, 2003). It is also clear that doctors can support addicted individuals in making plans to quit: for example, with the provision of information on services that provide support, or in some cases prescribing medication. One particular technique used under the TTM is referred to as **motivational interviewing** and involves the practitioners using a variety of methods to develop the motivation of the individual to attempt abstinence:

- giving advice: identifying the problem and the need for change
- removing impediments to change: problem-solving
- providing choices
- decreasing desirability of not changing: promotion of benefits of change
- empathy
- accurate behaviour feedback: identify problem behaviours
- clarifying goals.

In fact, the TTM is thought by many to have revolutionised treatment of addiction, particularly smoking, by providing a careful framework in which practitioners can guide individuals from one stage to the next. Indeed some reports suggest that treatment strategies that incorporate the model can improve the rates of giving up smoking by up to 20%. However, the model is not without its criticisms, which were most recently outlined in some detail by West (2005), who suggests that the model is merely stating common sense and that the levels are too arbitrary to be of value. He goes on to suggest that in addition to being of little value and ignoring other influences on behaviour, the model has, due to its extensive practitioner following, actually hindered the search for, and implementation of, other techniques. Despite this view, there are a number of psychosocial techniques that are used in treating addiction, either within the guidelines of the TTM or outside of it, and these will be considered next.

One widely known technique is that of cognitive therapy (Book 2, Section 3.3.1), which is used for a range of disorders and aims to identify and change dysfunctional thinking, behaviour and emotions. The cognitive therapist may approach the problem in a direct manner, presenting the individual with the irrational or dysfunctional thinking and questioning its origins. Importantly, the therapy tends to focus very much on the present situation rather than historical information. The ideal outcome is that the individual will recognise the dysfunctional thinking and clarify their goals to change the problem behaviour.

■ Considering the cognitive bias model of addiction, what type of dysfunctional thinking might cognitive therapy address?

□ The cognitive bias model suggests biases in attention and memory towards the subject of addiction and addiction-related stimuli. Cognitive therapy could therefore address these biases.

As well as cognitive therapy, addicted individuals may be given behaviour therapy (Book 1, Section 2.2.2) in which they are encouraged to identify the types of stimuli and environment they associate with their addiction and modify their behaviour to avoid them. Behaviour therapy can also incorporate methods such as **aversion therapy** and exercise therapy. Aversion therapy has been used in treatment of nicotine addiction and works by pairing the pleasant stimulus of smoking a cigarette with an unpleasant or aversive stimulus. The aversive stimulus of choice is normally the nausea induced by rapid smoking.

■ Aversion therapy is a form of classical conditioning in which the rapid smoking is the unconditional stimulus and the unconditional response is nausea. Can you identify the conditional stimulus and conditional response in this example?

□ The conditional stimulus is any stimulus associated with the smoking such as the sight of a cigarette, whilst the conditional response is nausea triggered by the sight of the cigarette.

Given that one of the key aims of behaviour therapy is to increase awareness of the stimuli associated with the addiction, with the view to reducing exposure to these stimuli, anti-addiction literature and advertisements must be carefully designed so as not to increase exposure to trigger stimuli. Figure 4.8 shows two anti-smoking adverts. Both are attempting to encourage people to stop smoking; however, they are very different in their approaches.

■ Which of the two adverts is most likely to trigger an urge to smoke in a smoker?

□ The first advert (a) shows smoke and cigarettes, both of which are likely to trigger craving in a smoker and therefore increase the likelihood of them having a cigarette. The second advert (b) does not show any smoking-related stimuli; it does not even use the words 'smoking' or 'cigarettes'.

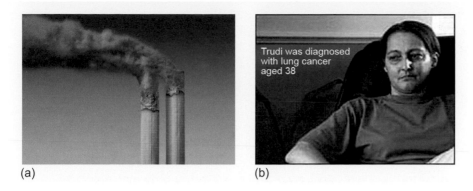
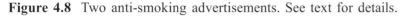

(a)   (b)

Figure 4.8 Two anti-smoking advertisements. See text for details.

Use of behaviour therapy to help individuals identify particular stimuli and learn to avoid them has support from many of the models outlined in Chapter 3 – to support the use of behaviour therapy merely requires the model to acknowledge the importance of associated stimuli or cues in craving and relapse.

■ Which models recognise the importance of cues associated with addiction in craving and relapse?

☐ The incentive sensitisation model recognises such importance through the transfer of the mesolimbocortical pathway response to associated cues. The cognitive bias model also recognises that addiction-related cues can cause the addicted individual to experience craving and thus increase the risk of relapse. Finally, the integrated approach taken by the excessive appetites model also supports use of behaviour therapy.

In addition to therapies that utilise classical conditioning, another form of behaviour therapy, called **contingency management therapy**, uses instrumental conditioning. This kind of treatment offers incentives or rewards to addicted individuals for meeting specific behavioural goals. Despite some considerable success in reducing drug use (Carroll and Onken, 2005), the cost of the schemes and the fact that effects diminish when the rewards are terminated means that such programmes are not widely used.

Exercise therapy is also used to help cessation and is believed to work by decreasing some of the acute withdrawal effects. However, as you will see in the following section on maintaining abstinence and preventing relapse, exercise may be useful beyond the initial cessation.

Whilst the individual therapies outlined above allow the counsellor or therapist to consider the specific situation and perspective of the addicted individual, they do not always represent a cost-effective and practical solution. Furthermore, even when ignoring financial and practical considerations, individual therapy does not provide the mutual and social support that can be obtained through group therapy.

Like individual therapy, group therapy may be administered through a professionally trained counsellor or psychologist. The content of professionally delivered group therapy can be very similar to that delivered in individual therapy and include cognitive and behavioural elements, in addition to building up social or peer support within the group.

It is, however, the self-help organisations that are most well known for delivering group therapy incorporating a high level of social or peer support. The most famous of these is of course Alcoholics Anonymous (AA), which was established in 1935 and developed the often cited 12-step programme for recovery. When AA was first established it took the, then unprecedented, step of delivering support through people who have experienced alcohol addiction but who are now abstaining from alcohol. The rationale behind this was that the problem drinker who no longer drinks is in a unique and powerful position to reach out to those who are still drinking.

The 12-step programme has now been adopted by a variety of other organisations ranging from Gamblers Anonymous (GA) and Narcotics Anonymous (NA) to Workaholics Anonymous (WA). Figure 4.9 shows the 12-step programmes from a variety of fellowships. Examine the figure and consider the questions below.

■ You have seen how prevention treatments can be specific or general; do you think the 12-step programme offered by WA is a specific intervention or a general one?

☐ Although the 12-step programme is offered through the fellowship of WA and some of the statements are related specifically to work it is basically following the same steps as AA, GA and NA.

Indeed the similarity of steps found in the different organisations supports the idea that all of these underlying addictions share similar causes and can be controlled by similar means.

■ All the 12-step programmes shown in Figure 4.9 suggest a belief in God or a higher power, which might relate to the group itself or the individual's sense of purpose; what might be a problem with this?

☐ Those that do not believe in such a higher power may be unable to follow the 12-step programme. It may also have the effect of making the individual feel that they can do nothing for themselves if the resolution of their addiction is all down to a higher force.

Despite vast amounts of anecdotal support for organisations such as AA and their 12-step programmes, empirical evidence is scarce. A study by Connors (1998) compared three different interventions for people addicted to alcohol. The first was a traditional 12-step programme in line with that delivered through AA, whilst the second used cognitive behaviour therapy (Book 2, Section 3.3.1), designed to teach coping skills and prevent relapse. The third and final intervention was a motivation enhancement therapy designed to increase motivation to change behaviour. The researchers found that people in all three groups significantly reduced drinking at a 12-month follow-up and results suggest that all three approaches were similar in effectiveness.

ALCOHOLICS ANONYMOUS

1 We admitted we were powerless over alcohol – that our lives had become unmanageable.
2 Came to believe that a Power greater than ourselves could restore us to sanity.
3 Made a decision to turn our will and our lives over to the care of God as we understood Him.
4 Made a searching and fearless moral inventory of ourselves.
5 Admitted to God, to ourselves and to another human being the exact nature of our wrongs.
6 Were entirely ready to have God remove all these defects of character.
7 Humbly asked Him to remove our shortcomings.
8 Made a list of all persons we had harmed, and became willing to make amends to them all.
9 Made direct amends to such people wherever possible, except when to do so would injure them or others.
10 Continued to take personal inventory and when we were wrong promptly admitted it
11 Sought through prayer and meditation to improve our conscious contact with God as we understood Him, praying only for knowledge of His will for us and the power to carry that out.
12 Having had a spiritual awakening as the result of these steps, we tried to carry this message to alcoholics and to practise these principles in all our affairs.

GAMBLERS ANONYMOUS

1 We admitted we were powerless over gambling – that our lives had become unmanageable.
2 Came to believe that a Power greater than ourselves could restore us to a normal way of thinking and living.
3 Made a decision to turn our will and our lives over to the care of this Power of our own understanding.
4 Made a searching and fearless moral and financial inventory of ourselves.
5 Admitted to ourselves and to another human being the exact nature of our wrongs.
6 Were entirely ready to have these defects of character removed.
7 Humbly asked God (of our understanding) to remove our shortcomings.
8 Made a list of all persons we had harmed and became willing to make amends to them all.
9 Made direct amends to such people wherever possible, except when to do so would injure them or others.
10 Continued to take personal inventory and when we were wrong promptly admitted it.
11 Sought through prayer and meditation to improve our conscious contact with God (as we understand Him), praying only for knowledge of His will for us and the power to carry that out.
12 Having made an effort to practise these principles in all our affairs, we tried to carry this message to other compulsive gamblers.

NARCOTICS ANONYMOUS

1 We admitted that we were powerless over our addiction, that our lives had become unmanageable.
2 We came to believe that a Power greater than ourselves could restore us to sanity.
3 We made a decision to turn our will and our lives over to the care of God *as we understood Him.*
4 We made a searching and fearless moral inventory of ourselves.
5 We admitted to God, to ourselves, and to another human being the exact nature of our wrongs.
6 We were entirely ready to have God remove all these defects of character.
7 We humbly asked Him to remove our shortcomings.
8 We made a list of all persons we had harmed, and became willing to make amends to them all.
9 We made direct amends to such people wherever possible, except when to do so would injure them or others.
10 We continued to take personal inventory and when we were wrong promptly admitted it.
11 We sought through prayer and meditation to improve our conscious contact with God *as we understood Him*, praying only for knowledge of His will for us and the power to carry that out.
12 Having had a spiritual awakening as a result of these steps, we tried to carry this message to addicts, and to practise these principles in all our affairs.

WORKAHOLICS ANONYMOUS

1 We admitted we were powerless over work – that our lives had become unmanageable.
2 Came to believe that a Power greater than ourselves could restore us to sanity.
3 Made a decision to turn our will and our lives over to the care of God as we understood God.
4 Made a searching and fearless moral inventory of ourselves.
5 Admitted to God, to ourselves, and to another human being the exact nature of our wrongs.
6 Became entirely ready to have God remove all these defects of character.
7 Humbly asked God to remove our shortcomings.
8 Made a list of all persons we had harmed, and became willing to make amends to them all.
9 Made direct amends to such people wherever possible, except when to do so would injure them or others.
10 Continued to take personal inventory and when we were wrong promptly admitted it.
11 Sought through prayer and meditation to improve our conscious contact with God as we understood God, praying only for knowledge of God's will for us and the power to carry that out.
12 Having had a spiritual awakening as the result of these steps, we tried to carry this message to workaholics, and to practise these principles in all our affairs.

Figure 4.9 An overview of the 12-step programmes offered for four different addictions. Note the similarity across addictions.

How do 12-step programmes fit then with the models of addiction discussed in the previous chapter? Remember there is no one-to-one mapping of model to treatment, given that all models and a variety of treatments may have some use, and so it is not possible to state definitively that this therapy is based around one model. However, it is plausible that a treatment that puts the individual and their beliefs at the centre of their recovery from addiction can be supported by the rational choice, cognitive bias, and excessive appetites models.

To summarise, there are a number of psychosocial treatments used in cessation. These range from individual therapy to self-help group support exemplified in organisations such as AA. These psychosocial treatments can begin before the addicted individual takes the step to initiate abstinence; indeed, much of the therapy is aimed at removing impediments to abstinence and increasing motivation and social support for attempting it. However, support will often remain in place after the initial detoxification, particularly in 12-step programme or other self-help interventions whereby involvement in the programme is considered key in relapse prevention.

4.6.2 Pharmacological treatments towards cessation

In addition to providing addicted individuals with the motivation and coping strategies to give up using their drug of choice or addictive behaviour through psychosocial interventions, pharmacological treatments may also be used. Unlike the psychosocial interventions, the latter are unlikely to be initiated prior to the decision to give up the drug or behaviour. This is largely because the current pharmacological treatments available are not thought to contribute to the motivation to attempt abstinence, but rather to support abstinence attempts once initiated and prevent relapse. Moreover, the pharmacological treatments are less frequently used in the treatment of behavioural addictions and therefore only really offer a viable treatment option for a subset of addictions.

■   Why is it not appropriate just to use a drug to decrease the motivation that drives the addiction?

☐   The mesolimbocortical pathway, which is important in motivation, is important in all types of motivation so you would not be able to alter motivation for the subject of the person's addiction without altering other motivations: for example, towards food or sex, or even getting out of bed in the morning.

The first hurdle during abstinence, and therefore the first point at which pharmacological interventions may be used, is coping with withdrawal symptoms. This is well documented for drug addictions such as alcohol and heroin, but less so for behavioural addictions like gambling. However, research does suggest that both types of addiction can share similar withdrawal symptoms. For example, heroin withdrawal symptoms include restlessness, muscle and bone pain, insomnia, diarrhoea, vomiting, and cold flushes, whilst withdrawal from gambling addiction is formally known to include just restlessness and irritability (DSM-IV-TR; APA, 2000). However, reports from treatment programmes suggest that headaches, abdominal pain, diarrhoea, cold sweats, tremors and nightmares are also present in the first few days following abstinence (Cunningham-Williams et al., 2009). This supports the idea of similar biological effects for these different subjects of addiction.

When treating this acute withdrawal, the severity of the symptoms affects whether treatment is in the home or hospital settings. For example, alcohol withdrawal can be quite severe and include seizures or cardiac problems, which could be life-threatening. These serious withdrawal symptoms may require hospitalisation, but others (including those listed above) can be treated in the home with symptomatic medication, meaning medication to relieve the symptoms, such as the pain, rather than the addiction.

Despite the potential of medication to relieve the symptoms of acute withdrawal, this early stage of abstinence represents a very significant time point in recovery and, as such, is a major challenge to both the individual and those supporting them. One approach to improving the chances of maintaining abstinence beyond this acute withdrawal period is to reduce or prevent the withdrawal effects from occurring at all, rather than treat them when they occur.

This type of intervention is normally reserved for drug addictions and requires the individual to be transferred onto another drug, similar in action to the one they are addicted to. The key difference is that this substitution drug has a less severe withdrawal syndrome, making the progression to abstinence more bearable. This is most commonly used for the treatment of heroin or other opiate addictions and utilises both opioid agonists (Book 1, Section 2.4.2) and **partial agonists**. A partial agonist can also bind to the receptor sites for the natural neurotransmitter and mimic its actions but it does so less effectively than the neurotransmitter or full agonist.

Methadone (Figure 4.10) is the opioid agonist routinely used as a substitution treatment in heroin addiction. The normally injected heroin is replaced with orally administered methadone, which acts at the same receptors in the brain as heroin, but does not induce the unpleasant withdrawal associated with heroin. The fact that methadone is orally administered means that its rate of entry into and removal from the brain, although still short-term, is less transient than with heroin. Given the importance of the transient increase in creating the feeling of being high, methadone does not elicit as strong a sense of euphoria as heroin, although some individuals may attempt to inject it to increase the euphoria experienced. By gradually transferring the addicted individual to oral methadone, and then reducing the dose, a drug-free state can be achieved with fewer negative effects.

More recently, buprenorphine, a partial opioid agonist, has been used instead of methadone. It has virtually no withdrawal effects, making it a highly desirable treatment if minimising acute withdrawal is the goal. However, being a partial agonist means that the high that is obtained from buprenorphine is also reduced, resulting in addicted individuals preferring methadone treatment.

Similar substitution treatments to aid cocaine detoxification have been less forthcoming. Amphetamine has been posited as one possible substitution drug suitable for use in cocaine detoxification (Gorelick et al., 2004) but this has never really been a viable option.

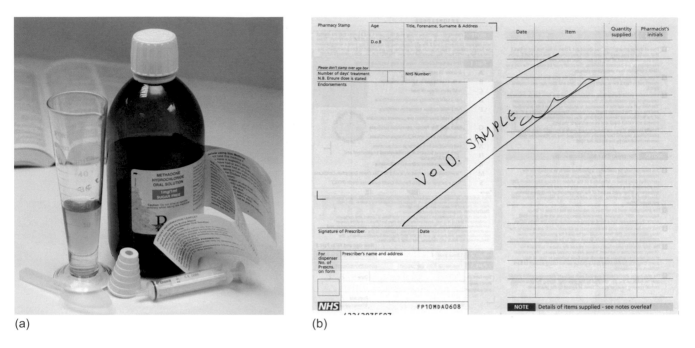

(a)   (b)

Figure 4.10 (a) Methadone for oral administration. (b) Prescriptions for methadone are written on blue prescription paper as opposed to the standard green. This indicates that the medication is for daily instalments and there is an additional table to be completed by the pharmacist when each instalment is collected.

■ Can you think of the problem with using amphetamine to treat cocaine addiction?

□ Amphetamine is also abused and could be addictive, so offers little advantage over cocaine.

To resolve the problem of treating cocaine addiction with amphetamine, scientists have suggested combining amphetamine with another chemical, which reduces its abuse liability, whilst maintaining its effects of reducing cocaine intake (Negus et al., 2009). This form of treatment is in the very early stages and is therefore still under investigation.

Another potential treatment to aid cocaine detoxification focuses on both the effects it can have on motivation and the depression-like symptoms of withdrawal.

■ From your knowledge of the effects of cocaine at the synapse and of depression (from Book 2), what two neurotransmitters do you think will be involved in these motivation and depressive experiences?

□ The effects on motivation are likely to be mediated by dopamine, levels of which are increased by cocaine. The depressive effects are likely to be mediated by serotonin, levels of which are reduced in depression and increased by most antidepressant medications.

Evidence from animal studies has suggested that by choosing a treatment that causes the release of dopamine and (to a lesser extent) serotonin, intake of cocaine is reduced (Negus et al., 2009). This treatment could have the effect of decreasing intake to such an extent that withdrawal from cocaine is so mild that abstinence is achieved more easily.

An alternative to treatment with agonists or drugs eliciting similar effects is to treat with an antagonist, which basically means a drug that binds to the same site in the brain as the addictive drug, but has no effect there, similar to a key that fits a lock but will not turn to open the door. An antagonist prevents the addictive drug binding to the receptors. A particularly successful antagonist treatment has been naltrexone, which blocks the effects of heroin (Book 1, Section 2.4.2). However, unlike methadone, naltrexone offers no rewarding effects whatsoever and therefore, perhaps unsurprisingly, addicted individuals prefer treatment with methadone (O'Brien, 2008). Incidentally, although naltrexone is approved for use in opiate dependence and overdose situations due to it being active at the same receptors as heroin, it is normally used in alcohol addiction where it is thought to reduce the rewarding effects of alcohol (Ivanov et al., 2006).

As well as blocking effects of a drug at the same receptor site or transferring to a more desirable drug, it is possible to block a drug-induced high by action at a different site within the relevant neural circuitry. For example, a number of drugs found to increase inhibition of the mesolimbocortical pathway, by acting to increase levels of GABA (an inhibitory neurotransmitter) or decrease levels of glutamate (an excitatory neurotransmitter), offer useful avenues of investigation.

Although a variety of these mechanisms have shown promise in the laboratory using rats and in some instances in human studies (Ivanov et al., 2006), the majority have not yet made the transition to clinical use. On the other hand, other medications, such as modafinil, which is used in the sleep disorder narcolepsy, have been found to decrease cocaine-induced euphoria in human studies, although the mechanism of this action is unclear (O'Brien, 2008).

Even if blocking the euphoric effects of the drug or reducing withdrawal can aid in reaching a drug-free state, it is the maintenance of this state that represents the biggest challenge in treating addiction and one for which the situation looks rather more bleak. Craving for a drug is strongly associated with relapse into drug use and therefore a key area for development is in craving-reducing drugs. In the laboratory, craving is normally measured in terms of self-administration (with animals pressing a lever to receive the drug) and a number of drugs have been shown to decrease cocaine administration and therefore may be effective in blocking craving. These include modafinil, buprenorphine and GABA agonists, all of which have been mentioned above.

As with the psychosocial treatments, these treatments cannot be considered as resting on one specific model of addiction development. However, the emphasis of a number of pharmacological treatments is on withdrawal, which is the focus of one model in particular.

■   Which model of addiction assumes a role of withdrawal in repeated drug use?

    ☐   The opponent motivational process model emphasises the role of the negative effects in addiction, as opposed to the strong desires for the positive effects.

By contrast, drug treatments aimed at suppressing the craving experiences are more in line with the incentive sensitisation and cognitive bias models. Finally, there has even been talk of a vaccine being developed for addiction (Killian et al., 1978). A vaccine would offer a safe treatment which could be administered over a few months and yet have longer-lasting effects. The science behind the vaccine is that its administration would result in antibodies in the body that are able to capture the drug before it enters the central nervous system, thus reducing levels available in the brain and therefore reduce the reinforcing effect on the individual (Moreno and Janda, 2009) and, as a consequence, the likelihood of repeated use. However, it would do this in a drug-specific manner; that is, a morphine vaccine would only decrease the administration of morphine and therefore may have limited use if an individual uses more than one type of drug, which is reasonably common. Despite the idea initially receiving attention many years ago, progress has been very slow and further advances are still required in vaccine strategies before any treatments are likely to be successfully developed.

4.6.3 Alternative treatments in cessation

Sections 4.6.1 and 4.6.2 examined the psychosocial and pharmacological interventions that may be used to help people achieve detoxification and long-term abstinence. However, there is one class of interventions that does not sit comfortably in either of these categories and yet is widely used as cessation treatment. This includes, for example, increased exposure to natural reinforcers, such as sweet foods, enriched environments or exercise equipment, all of which may activate the dopaminergic pathways, therefore replacing the need for the addictive drug or behaviour and therefore may be helpful in relapse prevention. However, there are other treatments where the underlying mechanism is less clear. This section will consider two examples: hypnotherapy and acupuncture.

Hypnotherapy

Hypnotherapy is widely promoted as a method to aid smoking cessation in particular, but it has also been used in group therapy for opiate addiction with some success. Although the underlying mechanism of *how* hypnotherapy achieves its effects is unclear, it is thought to increase the will to stop using, or increase focus on other cessation treatments. One particular hypnotherapy intervention developed by Spiegel and colleagues in 1993 sees the use of hypnotherapy to modify perceptions of smoking.

    ■   What type of psychosocial cessation intervention also tries to modify the person's perceptions or beliefs about their addiction?

    ☐   Cognitive therapy also tries to alter perceptions that the person may have about their habit or the consequences of changing their behaviour.

■ If the aim of this hypnotherapy is to modify perceptions of smoking, which models might support this type of treatment?

☐ The rational choice, cognitive bias and excessive appetites models all allow the behaviour of the addicted individual to be influenced by their thoughts and perceptions: for example, in a cost–benefit analysis.

During the hypnosis session, the smoker is instructed that: (a) smoking is a poison, (b) the body should be protected from smoking, and (c) there are advantages to life as a non-smoker. As with the psychosocial treatments and to an extent the pharmacological treatments, hypnotherapy can be used in the absence of a therapist, as some interventions may teach self-hypnosis. This can be useful in increasing compliance, because the addicted individual does not have to wait until their weekly appointment with a therapist, and in reducing cost of the treatment as fewer sessions with a professional therapist are required.

Unfortunately, there have been few carefully controlled studies of the effectiveness of hypnotherapy and reported success rates vary between 4% and 88% of smokers quitting following hypnotherapy (Abbot et al., 2009). At present, therefore, it is not possible to judge the value of this treatment, except to say that, whilst there is some indication of its success, careful research is now required.

Acupuncture

Acupuncture (Figure 4.11) involves the insertion of thin solid needles into specific points on the body. The needle can then be manipulated manually or using a small electrical current. Acupuncture has been of interest in treating addiction for many years, with the first discovery that it could decrease opiate withdrawal symptoms made by Wen and Cheung in 1973.

Acupuncture has been used to treat a wider variety of addictions than hypnotherapy. Moreover, there is also research into its mechanism of action and there has been some carefully controlled research into its efficacy. A study conducted at Yale Medical School (Avants et al., 2000) examined the effects of three different interventions on cocaine use in addicted individuals. Participants were randomly assigned to either an acupuncture condition, a needle insertion condition, or a relaxation condition and tested three times a week for the presence of drugs in their body, during the eight-week treatment period.

Figure 4.11 Acupuncture treatment.

■ During the needle insertion condition, participants had needles placed in position but no stimulation was applied; what is the purpose of this condition?

☐ It is a control condition for the acupuncture as the participants will experience the same needle insertion as the acupuncture group but no stimulation. By including this condition, it is possible to determine whether any effect seen is due to the acupuncture rather than the experience of having the needles inserted.

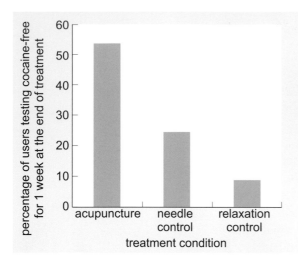

Figure 4.12 The effects of the three different conditions on cocaine use in the final week of an 8-week treatment period. The graph shows the percentage of users who were cocaine-free on three consecutive drugs tests during that week. Data adapted from Avants et al. (2000).

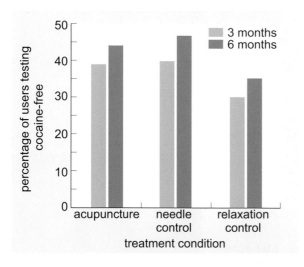

Figure 4.13 Data collected from a larger sample of cocaine users at 3 and 6 months after an 8-week intervention had finished. The number of participants remaining in each condition at these time points was approximately 100 meaning that each condition had similar retention rates and therefore any conclusions are not compromised by different withdrawal rates between the conditions. Data adapted from Margolin et al. (2002).

Figure 4.12 shows the results of this study from the final week of the intervention. At first glance, the results support the conclusion that acupuncture was effective in helping those addicted to cocaine abstain from taking the drug; however, the number of participants in each condition needs consideration. At the start of the study there were 82 participants, but by the end there were 52, of whom only 13 remained in the experimental (acupuncture) condition out of the initial 28 in this condition. Therefore it is possible that those less committed withdrew from the experiment and that the majority who withdrew did so from the experimental condition, which had a retention rate of just 46% compared to the other two conditions with 63% (needle insertion) and 81% (relaxation). As such, only those truly committed to stopping remained which may explain the higher success rate in this group. It should also be noted that a significant proportion dropped out of the needle insertion condition in contrast to the relaxation condition. This may relate to how well needle insertion is tolerated.

■ The results in Figure 4.12 were also taken from the final week of the treatment; do they tell you anything about long-term abstinence?

□ Not really; they better relate to the initial detoxification. A longer follow-up would be needed for information on long-term abstinence.

To further illustrate the need for suitable sample sizes and long-term measures of effectiveness, a similar, large-scale intervention was conducted by the same researchers using 620 participants addicted to cocaine with follow-up data collected three and six months after the intervention was completed. The results of this are shown in Figure 4.13 and are rather less conclusive, with a similar percentage being free from cocaine in both the acupuncture (experimental) and needle (control) group after both three and six months. The group with the lowest percentage of cocaine-free participants was the relaxation control group.

Despite these mixed findings on the efficacy of acupuncture as a cessation treatment, the finding that it can reduce withdrawal symptoms appears to be reliable, with both data from humans and other animals. Furthermore, the mechanism through which it does this is thought to involve modulation of the mesolimbocortical pathway, specifically decreasing dopamine release in response to drug stimuli, which could plausibly reduce the reinforcing effects of a drug and therefore the likelihood of repeating the behaviour.

- If acupuncture is associated with decreased withdrawal and stress (effects largely mimicked by relaxation techniques in Figure 4.9), which models might support its use?

□ Withdrawal is considered important in the opponent motivational process model. Stress is also considered important in the incentive sensitisation and excessive appetites model.

However, irrespective of support from addiction models, to date, there is little evidence to suggest that acupuncture is useful in actually achieving and maintaining abstinence.

4.7 Limitations and problems with cessation treatments

The critical consideration in using pharmacological agents in detoxification is that, by their design, they too may have some abuse potential and be addictive. The rationale is often that these treatment drugs have a lesser withdrawal and are less harmful such that an individual can essentially be weaned off them without experiencing the same negative effects seen with the drug they are addicted to. However, in some instances an individual can be maintained on these treatment drugs, as is commonly seen with methadone. For example, if methadone treatment is continued, rather than gradually reduced, the aim of the treatment is no longer achieving a drug-free state, but rather a heroin-free state. It could be argued that it is merely substituting one addiction for another.

This idea of substituting one addiction for another is also a criticism of some alternative therapies such as exercise therapy, which may be useful for inducing and maintaining abstinence. Recall from Chapter 1 the case of Peach, who was exercising at such a level that she was at risk from damaging her knees and ankles and had been advised to reduce or even stop this exercise.

Furthermore, this idea of substitution is even used as a criticism of some psychosocial interventions, specifically the 12-step programmes. It has been argued that the programmes themselves have cult-like qualities which encourage heavy reliance on the intervention in a similar manner to that seen in addictions. For the most part, these criticisms appear unfounded as the organisations have no hierarchy or financial exploitation of members, as might be seen with a cult. In addition, being enrolled on a 12-step programme is unlikely, in contrast to methadone or exercise, to lead to long-lasting harm as suggested in Chapter 1 as a defining characteristic of addiction. None the less, it does raise the concern that any type of treatment, not just pharmacological, must be evaluated carefully and the goals scrutinised.

Most people would probably agree that in an ideal situation the goal of cessation treatments should be that the addicted individual reaches a completely drug-free or problem-behaviour-free state. However, at least briefly, if not in the long term, most pharmacological substitution treatments actually involve replacing an illegal addictive drug for a legal one. Furthermore, if critics of the 12-step programmes are to be believed, these interventions also involve replacing a socially unacceptable and sometimes illegal addiction with a more socially acceptable one.

If the goal is merely to switch to this latter legal and more socially acceptable addiction then the aim of treatment has shifted from one of pure cessation to one of **harm reduction**. Harm reduction interventions aim to reduce the negative consequences of drug use or addictive behaviour across social, legal and health spectrums. One of the most commonly recognised harm reduction interventions is that of needle exchanges, where intravenous (or injecting) drug users (normally using heroin) are given access to clean needles for administration of heroin, thus decreasing the likelihood of contracting diseases such as hepatitis C or HIV. Harm reduction programmes have not just been introduced for heroin users, although this is the most successful area of implementation. Box 4.2 describes a harm reduction programme for those addicted to alcohol.

Box 4.2 Harm reduction interventions in addiction

Homeless shelters normally ban the presence of alcohol in an attempt to reduce problems with drunken clients. In 1997, a homeless shelter in Canada took the novel step of becoming a 'wet shelter', actually serving alcohol in a controlled fashion to alcohol-addicted clients (Podymow et al., 2006). By allowing the addicted individuals to drink in safety, the shelter aimed to reduce use of unsafe forms of alcohol (e.g. from industrial sources) and exposure to the unsafe external environment. After 16 months on this programme, the average number of visits to the emergency department had decreased by 41% and police encounters decreased by 51%. Perhaps more important was the fact that participants reported a decrease in overall alcohol consumption and improved compliance with medical and health care.

Thus when choosing treatments for addiction, it is important to consider whether the ultimate goal is a drug-free or problem-behaviour-free individual or one whose addiction may be transferred with the social, legal and health consequences removed or reduced. It may be that the goal will differ between individuals and different points in their addiction. For example, early cessation attempts may be with the aim of achieving a completely drug-free or problem-behaviour-free state, whilst later attempts may opt for shifting the addiction to a legal and socially acceptable form.

Now would be a good opportunity to briefly review the table you have completed for Activity 4.2. An example of the completed table can be downloaded from the SDK228 website.

- Looking at your table, are all treatments supported by at least one model?

- All treatments can be linked to at least one model and are often linked to more than one.

In much the same way that different factors may be more impor[t]
modelling particular addictions, different treatments may be mor[e]
treating different individuals. By acknowledging the variety of f[actors]
may affect addiction, it is possible to explore a wide range of tr[eatments. In]
particular, an individual may benefit from a biopsychosocial apj[roach to]
treatment, perhaps with some pharmacological intervention bein[g used in]
combination with other psychosocial treatments.

Activity 4.3 Treating addiction

(LOs 4.2 and 4.3) Allow 30 minutes

Now would be a good time to go to the multimedia map whe[re]
to a brief audio interview with an expert in addiction discussing the range o[f]
treatments available.

4.8 Wider issues in the treatment of addiction

Throughout this book, the similarities between a range of addictions,
involving both addictive drugs and behaviours, have been discussed. Indeed
you have seen that not only may these addictions share some common
neurobiology but also that they may all be treated with similar interventions.
However, addictions are separated in terms of the social and legal approaches
to the individual and the addiction, and this may have significant
consequences on the outcome for the person living with the addiction and for
those around them.

4.8.1 Social costs of addiction

One of the key differences amongst the addictions discussed is that they differ
vastly in the social costs associated with them. For example, the social stigma
surrounding heroin addiction is far greater than that surrounding other
addictions. This status cannot be explained by the social nuisance the
addiction causes, because this is likely to be significantly less than that caused
by alcohol. Rather it appears that the individual addicted to heroin breaks a
social contract with others by withdrawing from society and rejecting
conventional social relationships, thus eliciting disdain from other members of
society who perhaps also fear criminal acts being carried out to finance such
an addiction. Indeed some people still regard heroin addiction as an immoral
lifestyle choice when they might not apply the same label to a different
addiction.

The social stigma associated with different types of addiction undoubtedly
affects the probability of the addicted individual admitting to an addiction,
which in effect can hinder treatment of the problem. If an addicted individual
believes that they will suffer social exclusion if they admit to their addiction,
it is probable that they will avoid this admission. Indeed, so important is the
social cost of addiction that many interventions, not least the 12-step

programmes, require complete anonymity for members and this is likely to be a large factor in their perceived success.

4.8.2 Legal costs of addiction

The social stigma associated with addictions is undoubtedly linked to the legal position of an addiction. Addictions to some drugs and behaviours are legal. That is not to say that there is not some control exerted over these addictions in the form or licensing and purchase laws, but the act of using the drug or engaging with the behaviour can be legal. In contrast to this, use of drugs such as heroin and to a lesser extent drugs such as cannabis is largely illegal worldwide, although the penalties associated with use and enforcement of the relevant laws vary considerably between countries.

The categorisation of a substance as legal or illegal is perhaps a slight oversimplification; in fact, drug policy allows for three quite separate classifications:

1 Prohibition: Essentially outlawing the use, possession and supply of drugs of abuse, such that those found to contravene the law are liable to severe punishment including imprisonment.

2 Decriminalisation or depenalisation: A reduction in the criminality associated with offences concerning drugs of abuse. This is seen by many as a step towards legalisation.

3 Legalisation: A more lenient approach to drugs of abuse, whereby they are legalised although restrictions may still apply.

■ From the information presented in this chapter, what legal classification (prohibition, decriminalisation/depenalisation or legalisation) best describes the UK policy on nicotine and amphetamine and the Netherlands policy on cannabis.

☐ The UK policy on nicotine is best described as legalisation, whilst that on amphetamine is best described as prohibition. The Netherlands policy on cannabis is one of decriminalisation and *de facto* legalisation for small amounts of possession and use.

These different legal classifications mean that all potentially addictive behaviours can be legal, although some, such as gambling, may be subject to controls. In contrast, addictive drugs are for the most part illegal, with alcohol or nicotine being legal but subject to controls. It is of course possible that behavioural addictions such as sex addiction may become illegal (e.g. by using prostitutes or engaging in non-consensual sex) but the addiction itself can, in theory, be maintained legally, unlike a heroin addiction for example.

When we consider that all drug addictions can be justifiably grouped with these behavioural addictions, which have very different legal consequences, some uncomfortable questions are raised. Put crudely, why should the legal system control a heroin addict's supply of heroin but not a food addict's supply of food? Perhaps this is a little provocative, but it does raise an interesting point. When treating other addictions, the addicted individual does not risk prison for seeking out the object of their addiction, and sometimes not even social disdain. That is not to say that they are encouraged to feed their addiction, but it is, to a large extent, left in their hands. With addiction to illegal substances, however, the legal system attempts to control availability – can this difference be justified?

In the example above it would be reasonable to argue that the different social impacts of these addictions alone could justify the different legal positions: for example, the individual addicted to food is rarely seen committing crimes or engaging in other antisocial behaviours to obtain food. However, what about the person addicted to gambling? It is plausible they will turn to crime or other antisocial behaviour to fund their addiction and yet gambling, although regulated, is not controlled to the same level as heroin use.

By having different legal classifications, the different addictions are inevitably subject to different legal costs. Therefore an individual who is addicted to one drug or behaviour may pay a higher cost for their addiction than other addicted individuals. These higher legal costs, as with higher social costs, may serve as a deterrent to coming forward to admit to an addiction and, as such, they effectively represent an impediment to receiving treatment.

4.8.3 Creating a level playing field in addiction

One response to the differing social and legal costs of the different addictions is simply to attempt to create a level playing field. From a legal perspective this could mean applying similar levels of legal control to all drugs or behaviours that may become addictive. There are however a number of obvious problems with this. For example, given that the prohibition approach forms the basis of some effective prevention interventions and that there is an unknown risk of more widespread use if mass legalisation or even decriminalisation of currently illegal addictive drugs were to occur, such a change in the law is unlikely. Nevertheless, there may well be room for compromise.

A programme introduced in Switzerland for individuals addicted to heroin who had previously failed to become abstinent took an innovative approach to treating the addiction. Using a harm reduction approach, this programme sells heroin legally to these individuals, with the proviso that they use the heroin in a designated environment. Whilst the aim of the programme is largely to decrease the associated criminal activities, social problems and risk of secondary health problems (clean needles are supplied) with heroin addiction, it also in effect removes the criminality of using heroin in these controlled circumstances and thus may represent a slight levelling of the field. This project is still in its early stages and therefore it is not yet clear whether it will be successful in its aims.

In spite of this potential levelling, the legal position is likely to remain largely differentiated across addictions, but it is perhaps easier to level out the social cost playing field, which would still represent removal of a potential barrier to treatment.

Throughout this book you have learnt about addiction as a chronic, relapsing condition, which is influenced by a variety of psychosocial and biological factors. However, it is important not only to consider these factors but also to consider addiction in the wider context of mental health. Mental health problems have long been associated with social stigma. Take, for example, schizophrenia: in the past, people with schizophrenia were very much considered social outcasts and were persecuted because of their illness. Indeed, until relatively recently, those with a diagnosis of schizophrenia were viewed by the public as dangerous, and involuntary hospitalisation was considered an appropriate long-term treatment. Schizophrenia is a chronic relapsing disorder and in periods of relapse, individuals with this disorder may behave in a socially unacceptable manner – perhaps a similarity can be drawn with addiction. Fortunately, effective drug therapies for schizophrenia are now available and, although their efficacy varies, the illness can be reasonably well treated without long-term hospitalisation. As these advances in treatment have occurred and awareness of them increased, public opinion has also thawed and schizophrenia is no longer viewed so negatively.

Therefore, by examining the factors that may have contributed to the reduction in social stigma associated with schizophrenia, it may be possible to learn lessons on how to reduce the stigma of addiction.

■   What do you think might help to reduce the social stigma of addiction?

☐   It might help to increase public understanding of addiction and the factors that influence its development and treatment.

Therefore, although creating a level playing field in terms of social and legal factors for all addictions may be difficult, if not impossible, by seeing addiction as a mental health problem, much of the stigma could be removed, which may improve the likelihood of an addicted individual achieving long-term abstinence. You should by now recognise that in viewing addiction as a mental health condition, you are accepting that it can be influenced by a number of biological and psychosocial factors. As such, effective treatments may utilise psychosocial or biological approaches, but it is likely that a combination of both will be the most efficacious.

4.9   Final word

In this book you have learnt that addiction can take on many forms, ranging from sex, gambling, shopping, exercise and work to more familiar addictions such as that to nicotine or heroin. You have also learnt that addiction can be difficult to define but that a hallmark of addiction could be that the activity is taken to excess, such that it has a harmful effect on the addicted individual and those closest to him or her as well as wider society. Despite the wide range of addictions, all appear to have a neurobiological basis in the mesolimbocortical pathway which serves to control motivation, and all may be influenced by similar psychological and social factors. Although the exact transition from casual to addictive, compulsive behaviour is unclear, a number of models have been posited. With the wide range of addictions comes a wide range of treatments from traditional cognitive and behaviour therapy to pharmacological treatment of acute withdrawal. Crucially, treatment of addiction occurs within a wider context, which does not always accept the similarities between addictions and other mental health conditions. This presents a major barrier in treating all types of addiction. In this respect, you should now be armed to recognise the value of the biopsychosocial approach to understanding addiction.

4.10 Summary of Chapter 4

- Addictions can be treated with some degree of effectiveness with both psychosocial and pharmacological interventions.

- The psychosocial interventions include cognitive and behavioural elements and may be delivered by a professional therapist or through self-help organisations. These treatments may be initiated before detoxification to increase motivation and support. They may remain in place to prevent relapse and achieve long-term abstinence.

- Pharmacological treatments tend to be initiated during early withdrawal and are largely used during detoxification or, more controversially, maintenance.

- To date, few pharmacological treatments are used in relapse prevention, although some medicines do appear to decrease craving.

- Alternative therapies are available, although their efficacy remains unclear.

- An addicted individual may have a variety of different treatments, simultaneously or at different points in their recovery.

- Addiction treatment extends beyond the individual, and the effectiveness and availability of treatment is strongly affected by society and the legal system.

4.11 Learning outcomes

LO 4.1 Show that you recognise that addiction, like other chronic conditions, can be treated with prevention or cessation treatments. (KU1)

LO 4.2 Describe the different types of psychosocial treatments available for addiction and how they relate to the models of addiction. (KU4, CS1, CS2)

LO 4.3 Describe the different pharmacological treatments that may be used in treating addiction and how they relate to the models of addiction. (KU4, CS1, CS2)

LO 4.4 Describe how you might evaluate the effectiveness of an addiction treatment. (KU4, KU5, CS4)

LO 4.5 Show that you recognise the importance of the individual and society in treating addiction. (CS5)

4.12 Self-assessment questions

SAQ 4.1 (LO 4.1)

Using (i) smoking and (ii) cocaine use as examples, outline what possible interventions might be available to prevent or stop an individual smoking or using cocaine.

SAQ 4.2 (LOs 4.2 and 4.3)

What types of treatment would you consider when deciding how best to treat an individual addicted to (a) alcohol and (b) gambling?

SAQ 4.3 (LO 4.4)

How might you evaluate the effectiveness of a needle-exchange centre on drug addiction?

SAQ 4.4 (LO 4.5)

Give one example of a social and legal cost of heroin addiction. For each example suggest a way in which this could be reduced (if this is possible).

Answers and comments

Answers to SAQs

SAQ 1.1

It would appear to fit all seven criteria.

SAQ 1.2

Getting caught engaging in an illegal behaviour *might* occur at some stage in the future, as *might* financial ruin. Serious ill-health as a result of workaholism *might* follow but, if it does, this could well be years ahead. Sexually risky activities only *might* result in arrest, disease or injury. Of course, some negative consequences can be immediate, as in death from a drug overdose. Therefore, the use of the term 'hypothetical' is not meant to detract from certain real and serious dangers in addictive activities.

SAQ 1.3

(i) The injection of the drug; (ii) the high triggered by the drug; (iii) the sight of the drug and the procedure of injection; (iv) the high triggered by an inert substance (e.g. mild saline) being injected.

SAQ 1.4

At its roots, addictive behaviour is based upon a reward process rather than a process of avoiding aversion (*Note*: once established, there seemed to be an element of avoiding negative affect associated with it.)

SAQ 1.5

The drug-associated environment would be called a conditional stimulus.

SAQ 2.1

The three important areas are the ventral tegmental area, the nucleus accumbens (part of the striatum) and the prefrontal cortex (part of the cortex). The pathway originates in the ventral tegmental area and therefore the dopamine cell bodies would be found here. The neurons extend their axons to the nucleus accumbens and prefrontal cortex and therefore they would terminate in both of these regions.

SAQ 2.2

Given that heroin is an opioid agonist; its effects could be blocked by pre-treatment with an opioid antagonist. Also the action of heroin is to suppress GABA release from GABAergic neurons, so in theory, this effect could be counteracted by pre-treating with a GABA agonist. Either of these options would allow the activity of the dopaminergic neuron to be suppressed and thus dopamine release would be lowered.

SAQ 2.3

Cocaine blocks reuptake of dopamine from the synapse. Amphetamine also does this but in addition it causes dopamine to be released from the presynaptic neuron vesicles and pumped *out* of the reuptake channels *into* the synapse.

SAQ 2.4

No, the study shows that blood flow to the ventral striatum increased, which is not quite the same. The blood flow increase is likely to be due to increased activity in the area, and given that the region is stimulated by dopamine neurons in the VTA, it is likely that there was an increase in dopamine release but this cannot be confirmed definitely with fMRI.

SAQ 3.1

In the incentive sensitisation model, the dopamine response gradually becomes enhanced and this response indicates increased desire/wanting. In the opponent motivational process model, dopamine is critical for the positive experience and may also contribute to opponent process.

SAQ 3.2

By moving away, Ravi is likely to have left behind many of the cues that reminded him of taking heroin. Because these cues evoke a strong craving for the drug and may increase attention biases towards the drug, by moving away he is reducing his craving or desire for heroin.

SAQ 3.3

(a) Family studies can only tell you if addiction runs within families and not separate out the influences as environmental or genetic.

(b) Self-report studies rely on the individuals telling the truth about their addiction which they may not do due to the social and legal implications of any admission. In addition, the way in which they discuss their addiction may differ depending on who they are talking to.

(c) Animal studies cannot factor the many social and legal factors affecting addiction and therefore have limitations in investigating addiction beyond the biological perspective.

SAQ 3.4

Psychologically, this stress will leave them in a negative state and they may well return to their addiction to attempt to reach normality. At a neural level, the stressful period will induce increased CRF levels which are associated with drug intake.

SAQ 3.5

Adolescents are more impulsive and novelty-seeking. This is probably due to the different stages of maturity of the dopamine system and the prefrontal cortex, so the researchers might consider using young animals with a similar degree of maturation. As adolescents also have higher levels of sex hormones than other age groups, this could be factored in to any experiments.

SAQ 3.6

The individuals concerned may develop a sense of inevitability in their behaviour and, more widely, this group may be discarded by society as addicts. Commercially, it may also mean that those with vested interests such as dealers or those owning casinos might target people who they consider vulnerable. On a more positive note, it may also allow targeting of anti-addiction education and interventions.

SAQ 4.1

Note that the suggestions below are not exhaustive and you may have come up with others:

(a) There are a number of prevention interventions available for smoking such as anti-smoking school campaigns and television advertisements as well as purchase of cigarettes being legally controlled. Once a person has taken up smoking, they may receive help in quitting through a number of techniques but the most common cessation intervention is through the agonist treatment with nicotine patches or gum.

(b) As with smoking there can be a number of prevention interventions such as anti-drugs campaigns both in and outside of school. Cocaine is also prohibited by law and therefore there will be lower availability and a legal penalty for use which can act as a deterrent. Once use has begun, cessation treatments can include treatment of withdrawal symptoms during detoxification. There is no agonist treatment for cocaine addiction at present but drugs such as modafanil are effective in reducing cocaine intake. Individuals may also find alternative treatments such as hypnotherapy and acupuncture useful as well as attending self-help groups.

SAQ 4.2

For both gambling and alcoholism, there are a variety of psychosocial treatments available; both those delivered individually and as groups by professional therapists, as well as those delivered through 12-step programmes. For alcoholism, there are also pharmacological treatments including antagonists, although these are rarely used. Both addicted individuals could be treated with symptomatic medication for withdrawal symptoms.

SAQ 4.3

The aim of needle-exchange programmes is one of harm reduction, rather than achieving abstinence and so it would be important to assess whether the indirect adverse health effects have been reduced: for example, through blood tests for HIV and hepatitis C.

SAQ 4.4

Note that the answer given is one suggestion and you may have come up with others. A social cost of heroin addiction may be the social isolation incurred by the individual due to the stigma of their addiction. This could be overcome in part by widespread education about the nature of addiction and efforts made to reduce society stigma, with the view to encouraging individuals to come forward earlier for treatment. A legal consequence may be a criminal record for possession or for stealing to fund their addiction. One way to reduce this would be to legalise the drug but an alternative would be to encourage entry into programmes for treatment rather than a criminal record.

Comments on activities

Activity 1.2

You might have arrived at such factors as:

- curiosity and experimentation
- a search to find a solution to life's problems
- sexual desire
- imitation of role models
- peer pressure.

In the case of junk-food addiction, rather clearly, one needs to feed in order to survive, so this is somewhat different to the other initiating factors.

Activity 3.1

Note that although this activity continues into Chapter 4, you may like to compare your table to the example version for the information completed so far before you continue. This example version can be downloaded from the appropriate week in the study planner.

Activity 3.2

It is likely that you found you were quicker when you completed the reading of words where the colour of print was consistent with the word meaning. This is because we tend to process the meaning of the word before the colour of the print and therefore when they differ we find it very difficult to say the colour of the print.

Activity 4.1

Once you have completed your table, you should download an example version of the full table from the appropriate week of the study planner.

References

Abbot, N.C., Stead, L.F., White, A.R. and Barnes, J. (2009) 'Hypnotherapy for smoking cessation', *Cochrane Database of Systematic Reviews*, issue 2, no. CD001008. DOI: 10.1002/14651858.CD001008.

Agrawal, A. and Lynskey, M.T. (2008) 'Are there genetic influences on addiction: evidence from family, adoption and twin studies', *Addiction*, vol. 103, pp. 1069–81.

Alexander, B.K. (2000) 'The globalization of addiction', *Addiction Research*, vol. 8, pp. 501–26.

Alexander, B.K. (2008) *The Globalization of Addiction: A Study of Poverty of the Spirit*, Oxford, Oxford University Press.

Alexander, B.K. and Hadaway, P.F. (1982) 'Opiate addiction: the case for an adaptive orientation', *Psychological Bulletin*, vol. 92, pp. 367–81.

Alexander, B.K. and Schweighofer, A.R.F. (1988) 'Defining "addiction"', *Canadian Psychology*, vol. 29, pp. 151–62.

American Psychiatric Association (APA) (2000) *Diagnostic and Statistical Manual of Mental Disorders*, 4th edn, Text Revision (DSM-IV-TR).

Anczak, J.D. and Nogler, R.A. (2003) 'Tobacco cessation in primary care maximizing intervention strategies', *Clinical Medicine and Research*, vol. 1, no. 3, pp. 201–16.

Anderson, P., Chisholm, D. and Fuhr, D.C. (2009) 'Effectiveness and cost-effectiveness of policies and programmes to reduce the harm caused by alcohol', *The Lancet*, vol. 373, pp. 2234–46.

Avants, S.K., Margolin, A., Holford, T.R. and Kosten, T.R. (2000) 'A randomized controlled trial of auricular acupuncture for cocaine dependence', *Archives of Internal Medicine*, vol. 160, pp. 2305–12.

Baker, T.B., Japuntich, S.J., Hogle, J.M., McCarthy, D.E. and Curtin, J.J. (2006) 'Pharmacological and behavioural withdrawal from addictive drugs', *Current Directions in Psychological Science*, vol. 15, pp. 232–6.

Baumeister, R.F., Vohs, K.D. and Tice, D.M. (2007) 'The strength model of self-control', *Current Directions in Psychological Science*, vol. 16, pp. 351–5.

Bergh, C., Eklund, T., Sodersten, P. and Nordin, C. (1997) 'Altered dopamine function in pathological gambling', *Psychological Medicine*, vol. 27, pp. 473–5.

Black, D.W., Kehrberg, L.L.D., Flumerfelt, D.L. and Schlosser, S.S. (1997) 'Characteristics of 36 subjects reporting compulsive sexual behaviour', *American Journal of Psychiatry*, vol. 154, pp. 243–9.

Boileau, I., Dagher, A., Leyton, M., Gunn, R.N., Baker, G.B., Diksic, M. and Benkelfat, C. (2006) 'Modeling sensitization to stimulants in humans: an [11C] raclopride/positron emission tomography study in healthy men', *Archives of General Psychiatry*, vol. 63, pp. 1386–95.

Booth Davies, J. (1997) *The Myth of Addiction*, Amsterdam, Harwood Academic Publishers.

Boyer, M. and Dickerson, M. (2003) 'Attentional bias and addictive behaviour: automaticity in a gambling-specific modified Stroop task', *Addiction*, vol. 98, pp. 61–70.

Brook, J.S., Zhang, C., Finch, S.J. and Brook, D.W. (2010) 'Adolescent pathways to adult smoking: ethnic identity, peer substance use and antisocial behavior', *The American Journal on Addictions*, vol. 19, pp. 178–86.

Buchmann, A.F., Schmid, B., Blomeyer, D., Becker, K., Treutlein, J., Zimmermann, U.S. et al. (2009) 'Impact of age at first drink on vulnerability to alcohol-related problems: testing the marker hypothesis in a prospective study of young adults', *Journal of Psychiatric Research*, vol. 43, pp. 1205–12.

Carnes, P. (2001) *Out of the Shadows: Understanding Sexual Addiction* (3rd edn), Center City, MN, Hazelden Information and Educational Services.

Carroll, K.M. and Onken, L.S. (2005) 'Behavioral therapies for drug abuse', *American Journal of Psychiatry*, vol. 162, pp. 1452–60.

Carroll, M.E., Anker, J.J. and Perry, J.L. (2009) 'Modelling risk factors for nicotine and other drug abuse in the preclinical laboratory', *Drug and Alcohol Dependence*, vol. 104, pp. S70–S78.

Chambers, R.A., Taylor, J.R. and Potenza, M.N. (2003) 'Developmental neurocircuitry of motivation in adolescence: a critical period of addiction vulnerability', *American Journal of Psychiatry*, vol. 160, pp. 1041–52.

Chapman, C.L. and de Castro, J.M. (1990) 'Running addiction: measurement and associated psychological characteristics', *The Journal of Sports Medicine and Physical Fitness*, vol. 30, pp. 283–90.

Cheever, S. (2008) *Desire: Where Sex Meets Addiction*, New York, Simon and Schuster.

Concise Oxford English Dictionary (2009) (11th edn revised) Soanes, C. and Stevenson, A. (eds), Oxford, Oxford University Press.

Connors, G.J. (1998) 'Overview of Project MATCH', *The Addictions Newsletter*, vol. 5, pp. 6–7.

Cunningham-Williams, R.M., Gattis, M.N., Dore, P.M., Shi, P. and Spitznagel, E.L. (2009) 'Towards DSM-V: considering other withdrawal-like symptoms of pathological gambling disorder', *International Journal of Methods in Psychiatric Research*, vol. 18, pp. 13–22.

Department of Health (2009) 'Statistics from the National Drug Treatment Monitoring System (NDTMS) 1 April 2007–31 March 2008' [online], National Treatment Agency for Substance Misuse, http://www.nta.nhs.uk/uploads/ ndtms_annual_report_2007_08_011008.pdf (Accessed August 2010).

DiClemente, C. (2003) *Addiction and Change: How Addictions Develop and Addicted People Recover*, New York, Guilford Press.

Faggiano, F., Vigna-Taglianti, F.D., Versino, E., Zambon, A., Borraccino, A. and Lemma, P. (2008) 'School-based prevention for illicit drugs use: a systematic review', *Preventive Medicine*, vol. 46, pp. 385–96.

Fast, D., Shoveller, J., Shannon, K. and Kerr, T. (2010) 'Safety and danger in downtown Vancouver: understandings of place among young people entrenched in an urban drug scene', *Health and Place*, vol. 16, pp. 51–60.

Field, M. and Cox, W.M. (2008) 'Attentional bias in addictive behaviors: a review of its development, causes, and consequences', *Drug and Alcohol Dependence*, vol. 97, pp. 1–20.

Friedman, P. (2009) *Diary of an Exercise Addict*, Guilford, CT, Globe Pequot Press.

Giugliano, J.R. (2008) 'Sexual impulsivity, compulsivity or dependence: an investigative inquiry', *Sexual Addiction and Compulsivity*, vol. 15, pp. 139–57.

Gold, S.N. and Heffner, C.L. (1998) 'Sexual addiction: many conceptions, minimal data', *Clinical Psychology Review*, vol. 18, pp. 367–81.

Goodman, A. (2008) 'Neurobiology of addiction: an integrative review', *Biochemical Pharmacology*, vol. 75, pp. 266–322.

Gorelick, D.A., Gardner, E.L. and Xi, Z.X. (2004) 'Agents in development for the management of cocaine abuse', *Drugs*, vol. 64, pp. 1547–73.

Grant, J.E., Kim, S.W., Odlaug, B.L., Buchanan, S.N. and Potenza, M.N. (2009) 'Late-onset pathological gambling: clinical correlates and gender differences', *Journal of Psychiatric Research*, vol. 43, pp. 380–7.

Griffiths, M. (2005) 'Workaholism is still a useful construct', *Addiction Research and Theory*, vol. 13, pp. 97–100.

Hand, T. and Rishiraj, A.S. (2009) 'Seizures of Drugs in England and Wales, 2008/09', Home Office Statistical Bulletin [online], Home Office; http://rds.homeoffice.gov.uk/rds/pdfs09/hosb1609.pdf (Accessed August 2010).

Ifland, J.R., Preuss, H.G., Marcus, M.T., Rourke, K.M., Taylor, W.C., Burau, K. et al. (2009) 'Refined food addiction: a classic substance use disorder', *Medical Hypotheses*, vol. 72, pp. 518–26.

Ivanov, I.S., Schulz, K.P., Palmero, R.C. and Newcorn, J.H. (2006) 'Neurobiology and evidence-based biological treatments for substance abuse disorders', *CNS Spectrums*, vol. 11, pp. 864–77.

Johnson, C.A., MacKinnon, D.P. and Pentz, M.A. (1996) 'Breadth of program and outcome effectiveness in drug abuse prevention', *American Behavioral Scientist*, vol. 39, pp. 884–96.

Killian, A., Bonese, K., Rothberg, R.M., Wainer, B.H. and Schuster, C.R. (1978) 'Effects of passive immunization against morphine on heroin self-administration', *Pharmacology Biochemistry and Behaviour*, vol. 9, pp. 347–52.

Klanecky, A.K., Salvi, S. and McChargue, D.E. (2009) 'Coerced childhood sexual abuse moderates the association between cigarette smoking initiation and college drug use frequency', *The American Journal on Addictions*, vol. 18, pp. 363–6.

Klein, A.A. (2007) 'Suppression-induced hyperaccessibility of thoughts in abstinent alcoholics: a preliminary investigation', *Behaviour Research and Therapy*, vol. 45, pp. 169–77.

Kobus, K. and Henry, D.B. (2010) 'Interplay of network position and peer substance use in early adolescent cigarette, alcohol, and marijuana use', *Journal of Early Adolescence*, vol. 30, pp. 225–45.

Koob, G.F. and Le Moal, M. (2008) 'Neurobiological mechanisms for opponent motivational processes in addiction', *Philosophical Transactions of the Royal Society of London – Series B: Biological Sciences*, vol. 363, pp. 3113–23.

Kozlowski, L.T., Wilkinson, A., Skinner, W., Kent, C., Franklin, T. and Pope, M. (1989) 'Comparing tobacco cigarette dependence with other drug dependencies', *Journal of the American Medical Association*, vol. 261, pp. 898–901.

Lim, S.-Y., Evans, A.H. and Miyasaki, J.M. (2008) 'Impulse control and related disorders in Parkinson's disease', *Annals of the New York Academy of Sciences*, vol. 1142, pp. 85–107.

Liu, Z., Richmond, B.J., Murray, E.A., Saunders, R.C., Steenrod, S., Stubblefield, B.K. et al. (2004) 'DNA targeting of rhinal cortex D2 receptor protein reversibly blocks learning of cues that predict reward', *Proceedings of the National Academy of Sciences USA*, vol. 101, pp. 12336–41.

MacCoun, R. and Reuter, P. (1997) 'Interpreting Dutch cannabis policy: reasoning by analogy in the legalization debate', *Science*, vol. 278, pp. 47–52.

Maltz, W. and Maltz, L. (2008) *The Porn Trap*, London, HarperCollins.

Mantsch, J.R., Yuferov, V., Mathieu-Kia, A.M. and Kreek, M.J. (2004) 'Effects of extended access to high versus low cocaine doses on self-administration, cocaine-induced reinstatement and brain mRNA levels in rats', *Psychopharmacology (Berl)*, vol. 175, pp. 26–36.

Margolin, A., Kleber, H.D., Avants, S.K., Konefal, J., Gawin, F., Stark, E. et al. (2002) 'Acupuncture for the treatment of cocaine addiction: a randomized controlled trial', *Journal of the American Medical Association*, vol. 287, pp. 55–63.

Marissen, M.A., Franken, I.H., Waters, A.J., Blanken, P., van den Brink, W. and Hendriks, V.M. (2006) 'Attentional bias predicts heroin relapse following treatment', *Addiction*, vol. 101, pp. 1306–12.

McIntyre, R.S., McElroy, S.L., Konarski, J.Z., Soczynska, J.K., Wilkins, K. and Kennedy, S.H. (2007) 'Problem gambling in bipolar disorder: results from the Canadian community health survey', *Journal of Affective Disorders*, vol. 102, pp. 27–34.

Melzack, R. (1988) 'The tragedy of needless pain: a call for social action', in Dubner, R. Gubner, G.F. and Bond, M.R. (eds) *Proceedings of the Vth World Congress on Pain*, Amsterdam, Elsevier Science Publishers, pp. 1–11.

Melzack, R. and Wall, P (1996) *The Challenge of Pain*, Harmondsworth, Penguin Books.

Merikangas, K.R., Stolar, M., Stevens, D.E., Goulet, J., Preisig, M.A., Fenton, B. et al. (1998) 'Familial transmission of substance use disorders', *Archives of General Psychiatry*, vol. 55, pp. 973–9.

Miech, R. and Chilcoat, H. (2007) 'The formation of a socioeconomic disparity: a case study of cocaine and marijuana use in the 1990s', *American Journal of Preventive Medicine*, vol. 32, pp. S171–6.

Moreno, A.Y. and Janda, K.D. (2009) 'Immunopharmacotherapy: vaccination strategies as a treatment for drug abuse and dependence', *Pharmacology and Biochemistry of Behaviour*, vol. 92, pp. 199–205.

Morgan, D., Grant, K.A., Gage, H.D., Mach, R.H., Kaplan, J.R., Prioleau, O. et al. (2002) 'Social dominance in monkeys: dopamine D_2 receptors and cocaine self-administration', *Nature Neuroscience*, vol. 5, pp. 169–74.

Moskowitz, D.A. and Roloff, M.E. (2007) 'The ultimate high: sexual addiction and the bug chasing phenomenon', *Sexual Addiction and Compulsivity*, vol. 14, pp. 21–40.

Negus, S.S., Baumann, M.H., Rothman, R.B., Mello, N.K. and Blough, B.E. (2009) 'Selective suppression of cocaine- versus food-maintained responding by monoamine releasers in rhesus monkeys: benzylpiperazine, (+)phenmetrazine, and 4-benzylpiperidine', *Journal of Pharmacology and Experimental Therapy*, vol. 329, pp. 272–81.

Nesse, R.M. and Berridge, K.C. (1997) 'Psychoactive drug use in evolutionary perspective', *Science*, vol. 278, pp. 63–6.

O'Brien, C.P. (2008) 'Evidence-based treatments of addiction', *Philosophical Transactions of the Royal Society of London – Series B: Biological Sciences*, vol. 363, pp. 3277–86.

Orford, J. (2001) 'Addiction as excessive appetite', *Addiction*, vol. 96, pp. 15–31.

Pecina, S., Schulkin, J. and Berridge, K.C. (2006) 'Nucleus accumbens corticotropin-releasing factor increases cue-triggered motivation for sucrose reward: paradoxical positive incentive effects in stress?', *BMC Biology*, vol. 4, p. 8.

Peele, S. and Degrandpre, R.J. (1998) 'Cocaine and the concept of addiction: environmental factors in drug compulsions', *Addiction Research*, vol. 6, pp. 235–63.

Pérez, A., Ariza, C., Sánchez-Martínez, F. and Nebot, M. (2010) 'Cannabis consumption initiation among adolescents: A longitudinal study', *Addictive Behaviors*, vol. 35, pp. 129–34.

Petraitis, J., Flay, B.R. and Miller, T.Q. (1995) 'Reviewing theories of adolescent substance use: organizing pieces in the puzzle', *Psychological Bulletin*, vol. 117, pp. 67–86.

Pfaus, J.G and Philips, A.G. (1991) 'Role of dopamine in anticipatory and consummatory aspects of sexual behavior in the male rat', *Behavioral Neuroscience*, vol. 105, pp. 727.

Pfaus, J.G., Damsma, G., Nomikos, G.G., Wenkstern, D.G., Blaha, C.D., Phillips, A.G. and Fibiger, H.C. (1990) 'Sexual behavior enhances central dopamine transmission in the male rat', *Brain Research*, vol. 530, pp. 345–8.

Podymow, T., Coyle, D., Yetisir, E. and Wells, G. (2006) 'Shelter-based managed alcohol administration to chronically homeless people addicted to alcohol', *Canadian Medical Association Journal*, vol. 174, pp. 45–9.

Prochaska, J.O. and DiClemente, C.C. (1983) 'Stages and processes of self-change of smoking: toward an integrative model of change', *Journal of Consulting and Clinical Psychology*, vol. 51, pp. 390–5.

Putnam, D.E. (2000) 'Initiation and maintenance of online sexual compulsivity: Implications for assessment and treatment', *CyberPsychology and Behavior*, vol. 3, pp. 553–63.

Queri, S., Erbas, B. and Soyka, M. (2007) 'Treatment prevalence in pathological gambling', *Fortschritte der Neurologie Psychiatrie*, vol. 75, pp. 458–62.

Reuter, J., Raedler, T., Rose, M., Hand, I., Glascher, J. and Buchel, C. (2005) 'Pathological gambling is linked to reduced activation of the mesolimbic reward system', *Nature Neuroscience*, vol. 8, pp. 147–8.

Rivier, C., Bruhn, T. and Vale, W. (1984) Effect of ethanol on the hypothalamic-pituitary-adrenal axis in the rat: role of corticotropin-releasing factor (CRF)', *Journal of Pharmacology and Experimental Therapeutics*, vol. 229, pp. 127–31.

Robins, L.N., Helzer, J.E. and Davis, D.H. (1975) 'Narcotic use in Southeast Asia and afterward', *Archives of General Psychiatry*, vol. 32, pp. 955–61.

Robinson, B.E. (2007) *Chained to the Desk*, New York, New York University Press.

Robinson, T.E. and Berridge, K.C. (1993) 'The neural basis of drug craving: an incentive-sensitization theory of addiction', *Brain Research Reviews*, vol. 18, pp. 247–91.

Robinson, T.E. and Berridge, K.C. (2008) 'Review: The incentive sensitization theory of addiction: some current issues', *Philosophical Transactions of the Royal Society of London – Series B: Biological Sciences*, vol. 363, pp. 3137–46.

Rose, J.S., Dierker, L.C. and Donny, E. (2010) 'Nicotine dependence symptoms among recent onset adolescent smokers', *Drug and Alcohol Dependence*, vol. 106, pp. 126–32.

Ryan, M. (1996) *Secret Life: An Autobiography*, London, Bloomsbury.

Schneider, J. and Weiss, R. (2001) *Cybersex Exposed: Simple Fantasy or Obsession?*, Hazelden, Hazelden Publishing and Educational Services.

Schultz, W. (1998) 'Predictive reward signal of dopamine neurons', *Journal of Neurophysiology*, vol. 80, pp. 1–27.

Shahbazi, M., Moffett, A.M., Williams, B.F. and Frantz, K.J. (2008) 'Age- and sex-dependent amphetamine self-administration in rats', *Psychopharmacology (Berl)*, vol. 196, pp. 71–81.

Sheppard, K. (1993) *Food Addiction: The Body Knows*, Deerfield Beach, FL, Health Communications Inc.

Sheppard, K. (2000) *From the First Bite: A Complete Guide to Recovery from Food Addiction*, Deerfield Beach, FL, Health Communications, Inc.

Singer, J.L. (1993) 'Experimental studies of ongoing conscious experience', in Bock, G.R. and Marsh, J. (eds) *Experimental and Theoretical Studies of Consciousness*, Wiley, Chichester, pp. 100–22.

Smyth, B.P. and O'Brien, M. (2004) 'Children attending addiction treatment services in Dublin, 1990–1999', *European Addiction Research*, vol. 10, pp. 68–74.

Solomon, R.L. and Corbit, J.D. (1974) 'An opponent-process theory of motivation: I. Temporal dynamics of affect', *Psychological Review*, vol. 81, pp. 119–45.

Spiegel, D., Frischholz, E.J., Fleiss, J.L. and Spiegel, H. (1993) 'Predictors of smoking abstinence following a single-session restructuring intervention with self-hypnosis', *American Journal of Psychiatry*, vol. 150, pp. 1090–7.

Stewart, J., de Wit, H. and Eikelboom, R. (1984) 'Role of unconditioned and conditioned drug effects in the self-administration of opiates and stimulants', *Psychological Review*, vol. 91, pp. 251–68.

Swanson, J.M. and Volkow, N.D. (2003) 'Serum and brain concentrations of methylphenidate: implications for use and abuse', *Neuroscience and Biobehavioral Reviews*, vol. 27, pp. 615–21.

Tiffany, S.T. (1990) 'A cognitive model of drug urges and drug-use behavior: role of automatic and nonautomatic processes', *Psychological Review*, vol. 97, pp. 147–68.

Tobler, N. (1986) 'Meta-analysis of 143 adolescent drug prevention programs: quantitative outcome results of program participants compared to a control or comparison group', *Journal of Drug Issues*, vol. 16, pp. 537–67.

Tsuang, M.T., Bar, J.L., Harley, R.M. and Lyons, M.J. (2001) 'The Harvard Twin Study of Substance Abuse: what we have learned', *Harvard Review of Psychiatry*, vol. 9, pp. 267–79.

Vega, W.A., Aguilar-Gaxiola, S., Andrade, L., Bijl, R., Borges, G., Caraveo-Anduaga, J.J. et al. (2002) 'Prevalence and age of onset for drug use in seven international sites: results from the international consortium of psychiatric epidemiology', *Drug and Alcohol Dependence*, vol. 68, pp. 285–97.

Volkow, N.D., Ding, Y.S, Fowler, J.S., Wang, G.-J., Logan, J., Gatley, J.S. et al. (1995) 'Is methylphenidate like cocaine? Studies on their pharmacokinetics and distribution in the human brain', *Archives of General Psychiatry*, vol. 52, pp. 456–63.

Volkow, N.D., Wang, G.-J., Fowler, J.S., Logan, J., Gatley, S.J., Hitzemann, R. et al. (1997) 'Decreased striatal dopaminergic responsiveness in detoxified cocaine-dependent subjects', *Nature*, vol. 386, pp. 830–3.

Washton, A.M. and Stone-Washton, N. (1993) 'Outpatient treatment of cocaine and crack addiction: a clinical perspective', *NIDA Research Monograph*, vol. 135, pp. 15–30.

Wen, H. and Cheung, S. (1973) 'Treatment of drug addiction by acupuncture and electrical stimulation', *American Journal of Acupuncture*, vol. 1, pp. 71–5.

West, R. (2005) 'Time for a change: putting the Transtheoretical (Stages of Change) Model to rest', *Addiction*, vol. 100, pp. 1036–9.

West, R. (2006) *Theory of Addiction*, Oxford, Blackwell.

Whitesell, N.R., Beals, J., Mitchell, C.M., Manson, S.M., Turner, R.J. and the AI-Superpfp Team (2009) 'Childhood exposure to adversity and risk of substance-use disorder in two American Indian populations: the meditational role of early substance-use initiation', *Journal of Studies on Alcohol and Drugs*, vol. 70, pp. 971–81.

World Heath Organization (WHO) (2007) *The International Statistical Classification of Diseases and Related Health Problems*, (10th Revision) (ICD-10) Chapter V 'Mental and Behavioural Disorders' [online], http://apps.who.int/classifications/apps/icd/icd10online/ (Accessed August 2010).

Acknowledgements

Grateful acknowledgement is made to Katherine Leys for coordinating the Research Methods boxes throughout SDK228.

Grateful acknowledgement is also made to the following sources:

Figures

Figure 1.1: © Kay Sheppard; Figure 1.2: © Michael Falco Photography; Figure 1.3: © Peach Friedman; Figure 2.3: © American Association of Pharmaceutical Scientists; Figure 2.4: © Pfaus, J.G. et al. (2003) 'Sexual behaviour enhances central dopamine transmission in the male rat', *Brain Research*, Elsevier Science; Figure 2.8: © Cox, S.M.L. et al. (2009) 'Striatal dopamine responses to intranasal cocaine self-administration in humans', *Biological Psychiatry*, Society of Biological Psychiatry, Elsevier Science; Figure 2.9: With permission from the BMJ Publishing Group, photograph supplied by Dr Timo Krings, University Hospital of the TWTH Aachen; Figure 2.12: © Swanson, J.M. and Volkow, N.D. (2003) 'Serum and brain concentrations of methylphenidate: implications for use and abuse', *Neuroscience and Biobehavioural Reviews*, Elsevier Science; Figure 3.1: © Merikangas, K.R. et al. (1998) 'Familial transmission of substance use disorders', *Archives of General Psychiatry*, American Medical Association; Figure 3.2: © Edwin Remsberg/Alamy; Figure 3.3: © Schultz, W. (1998) 'Predictive rewards signal of dopamine neurons', *Journal of Neurophysiology*, American Physiological Society; Figure 3.4a: © Dimitriy Shironsoov/ iStockphoto; Figure 3.4b: © ImageState/Alamy; Figure 3.8: © Boyer, M. and Dickerson, M. (2003) 'Attention bias and addictive behaviour: automaticity in a gambling-specific modified Stroop task', *Addiction*, Society for the Study of Addiction to Alcohol and Other Drugs; Figure 3.9: © Shahbazi, M. et al. (2008) 'Age and sex dependent amphetamine self administration in rats', *Psychopharmacology*, Springer-Verlag GmbH & Co. KG; Figure 3.10: © Petraitis, J. et al. (1995) 'Reviewing theories of adolescent substance use: organising pieces in the puzzle', *Psychological Bulletin*; Figure 4.1: © Johnson, C.A. et al. (1996) 'Breadth of programme and outcome effectiveness in drug abuse prevention', *American Behavioural Scientist*; Figure 4.2: © Courtesy Grange Hill Fan Club; Figure 4.3: © University of Arizona; Figure 4.4: © Vega, W.A. et al. (2002) 'Prevalence and age of onset for drug use in seven international sites', *Drug And Alcohol Dependence*; Figure 4.5: © MacCoun, R. and Reuter, P. et al. (1997) 'Interpreting Dutch cannabis policy: reasoning by analogy in the legalization debate, *Science*; Figure 4.6: © Google Inc; Figure 4.7: © DiClemente, C.C. (2003) *Addiction and Change: How Addictions Develop and Addicted People Recover*, The Guildford Publications Inc; Figure 4.8a: © ASH – Action on Smoking and Health; Figure 4.8b: © news.bbc.co.uk; Figure 4.10a: © dan white/Alamy; Figure 4.11: © joefoxphoto/Alamy; Figure 4.12: © Avants, S.K. (2000) 'A randomized controlled trial of auricular acupuncture for cocaine dependence', *Archives of Internal Medicine*; Figure 4.13: © Margolin, A. et al. (2002) 'Acupuncture for the treatment of cocaine addiction: a randomized controlled trial', *Journal of the American Medical Association*.

SDK228 Team

Claire Rostron (*SDK228 Chair and Academic Editor*)
Basiro Davey (*Advisor*)
Viki Burnage (*SDK228 Manager*)
Helen Copperwheat (*SDK228 Assistant*)
Frederick Toates (*Block 1 Chair*)
Antonio Martins-Mourao
Saroj Datta (*Block 2 Chair*)
Heather McLannahan (*SDK228 Deputy Chair*)
Ellie Dommett (*Block 3 Chair*)
Katherine Leys (*Block 4 Chair*)

Consultants

Ilona Boniwell
Christine Heading
Margaret Swithenby

External assessor

Professor Neil Frude

Critical readers

Meg Barker
Mick McCormick
Ulf Wagner

Developmental testers

Elena Gammage
Jen Evans
Vicky Gaeta

Production team

Greg Black
Ann Carter
Martin Chiverton
Roger Courthold
Rebecca Graham
Sara Hack
Nicky Heath
Chris Hough
Carol Houghton
Roger Moore
Jon Owen
Judith Pickering
Brian Richardson

Federica Sacco
Bina Sharma

Indexer

Jane Henley

Library

Duncan Belks

Index

lumbar puncture 46

M

maintenance of addiction *see* development and maintenance of addiction
maintenance stage *96*
mesolimbocortical pathway 34, *35*, 36, 38, 46
  opponent motivational processes 64
  sensitisation 57, 58, 60
meta-analysis 90
methadone 103, *104*, 105, 109
methylphenidate 45, 60
microdialysis 36–7
mind, brain–mind 15
modafinil 105
models of addiction 51 2, *53*
  biomedical or 'disease' 53–66
  biopsychosocial approach *see* biopsychosocial model/ perspective
  psychological 66–73, 98
  transtheoretical 95, *96*, 97
mood 20, 21
morphine 22
motivation 25
  and behaviour 31–9
  and cocaine detoxification 104
  and context *60*
  incentive motivation 38, 57, 75
  opponent motivational processes 61–6, 106
motivational interviewing 97

N

naltrexone 105
Narcotics Anonymous 100, *101*
needle exchanges 110, 116, 120
'needle freak' 19, 29, 117
negative affect 21–2
negative reinforcement 32, 62, *64*
neuroadaptation 79, 80
neutral stimulus 25, 32, 58, 59, 72
nicotine addiction 7, 23
  anti-smoking advertisements 98, *99*
  aversion therapy 98

craving for 58, 59
dopamine levels 43
features of addiction *13*
hypnotherapy 106–7
legally required notices *92*
prevention measures 116, 119
treatment 20, *86*, 87, 97
withdrawal symptoms 19, 21
nominal data 71
novelty-seeking 55, 58, 61, 75, 119
nucleus accumbens (NAc) 34, *35*, 37, 46, 117

O

obsessive–compulsive disorder 23–4
opiates 3, 44
opioid agonists 103
opioids 38, 39, 43–4
opponent motivational process 61, **62**–6, 106
ordinal data 71

P

pain 22
Parkinson's disease 17
partial agonists 103
partial reinforcement schedule 26
peer association/pressure 17, 75, *82*
peer-based interventions 89–90
pharmacological withdrawal 19
physiological addictions 14, 15
positive reinforcement 32, 62, 63
positron emission tomography (PET) 41–3, *57*
pre-contemplation stage *96*, 97
prefrontal cortex (PFC) 34, *35*, 75, 117
preparation stage *96*
prevention 85
  general issues 85–8
  legislation-based 90–3
  limitations and problems 93–4
  school-based programmes 88–90
  smoking and cocaine use 116, 119
prohibition 112, 113
proximal factors 81, *82*
proxy measures 2

Prozac 24
psychoactive drugs 22–3
psychological addictions 14, 15, 22
psychological models of addiction
  cognitive bias model 69–73, 98
  rational choice model 66–8
psychosocial interventions 95, *96*, 97–100, *101*, 102
psychosocial model of addiction 78–80

Q

quantitative measurements 71

R

ratio measurement 70, 71
rational choice model 66–8
refined food products 6, *13*, 27
refusal skills training 89
reinforcers 32, 76
  see also **negative reinforcement; partial reinforcement schedule; positive reinforcement**
rejection reactions *38*
relapse 3, 11, 14
  after cessation *96*
  cues in 99
  schizophrenia 114
  stress-triggered 74, 84, 118
reuptake channels 40, *41*, 118
reward 26, 31, *59*
risk-taking 15–16

S

schizophrenia 114
school-based programmes 88–90
selective serotonin reuptake inhibitors 24
self-help organisations 100, *101*, 102, 109
self-hypnosis 107
self-image 20
self-medication 20, *76*
self-report studies 83, 118
sensitisation 57–8
  see also **incentive sensitisation**
sex addiction 2, 9–10, *13*